The Neuroscience of Everyday Life

Sam Wang, Ph.D.

PUBLISHED BY:

THE GREAT COURSES
Corporate Headquarters
4840 Westfields Boulevard, Suite 500
Chantilly, Virginia 20151-2299
Phone: 1-800-832-2412
Fax: 703-378-3819
www.thegreatcourses.com

Sam Wang, Ph.D.

Associate Professor of Molecular Biology and Neuroscience, Princeton University

Professor Sam Wang is Associate Professor of Molecular Biology and Neuroscience at Princeton University. He was born to immigrant parents in Cincinnati, Ohio, and moved to Riverside, California, with them, one brother, and one sister. In 1986, at the age of 19, he received his B.S. in Physics with honor at the California Institute of Technology, making him the youngest member of his graduating class. In 1994, he earned his Ph.D. in Neurosciences at Stanford University School of Medicine, where he did his research at the Hopkins Marine Station in Pacific Grove, California. His research concerned the signaling properties of calcium, a universal signaling ion in all cells, including neurons. His current research uses advanced optical methods to probe brain circuit function, with a focus on the cerebellum's role in perception, movement, and higher cognitive function.

After his doctoral research, Professor Wang continued his research at Duke University Medical Center, where he turned his attention to the molecular mechanisms by which neurons signal to one another using neurotransmitters. At this time he was a Grass Fellow in Neurophysiology at the Marine Biological Laboratory in Woods Hole, Massachusetts. It was also during this time that he was selected by the American Association for the Advancement of Science (AAAS) as a Congressional Science and Engineering Fellow. He spent a year away from the lab, on the staff of the U.S. Senate Committee on Labor and Human Resources. He handled reauthorization of the National Science Foundation and tracked federal education, science, and technology policy and budget trends for the late Senator Edward M. Kennedy. He also coordinated Mass NetDay96, a government-education-private partnership to bring Internet infrastructure to hundreds of public schools in Massachusetts.

After his work at Duke and on Capitol Hill, in 1997 Professor Wang moved to Bell Labs Lucent Technologies, where he worked as a postdoctoral member of the technical staff in the Physics Research Laboratory. With David Tank and Winfried Denk, he worked on the development and use of new technologies for probing living neural tissue by using multiphoton optical methods. After a brief stint at the Max Planck Institute for Medical Research in Heidelberg, Germany, he joined the faculty of Princeton University as an Assistant Professor in 2000 and was promoted to Associate Professor in 2006.

Professor Wang's research has resulted in the publication of more than 50 papers in leading peer-reviewed journals, including *Nature*, *Nature Neuroscience*, *Proceedings of the National Academy of Sciences*, *Neuron*, *Journal of Neuroscience*, and *Public Library of Science ONE*. He has won numerous awards for his research, including an Alfred P. Sloan Fellowship, the Rita Allen Foundation Young Scholars Fellowship, a Distinguished Young Investigator Award from the W. M. Keck Foundation, and a CAREER Award from the National Science Foundation. His research findings span from the function of single synapses to the architecture of whole brains. His work includes the discovery that learning mechanisms can, in the first minutes of the process, act like all-or-none switches, and that bird and mammalian brains share similar architectures for generating complex social relations. He is also known for innovative use of optical methods for probing the neural function of living brain tissue, both in vitro and in awake, behaving animals, by using multiphoton microscopy and light-sensitive "caged" neurotransmitters. His research has been featured on National Public Radio and in *The New York Times*.

In addition to his scientific research, Professor Wang is known for his public communication in the areas of neuroscience and statistics. In 2004 he pioneered the use of statistical meta-analysis to model the U.S. presidential election, establishing a method of polling analysis that was elaborated by dozens of hobbyists worldwide in 2004 and 2008. In 2008 he founded the Princeton Election Consortium, which came within 1 electoral vote of estimating the final outcome of the presidential race. This web-based modeling project attracted more than a million viewers and was featured on Fox News and in *The Wall Street Journal*.

Professor Wang is co-author with Sandra Aamodt of a bestselling popular book on neuroscience, *Welcome to Your Brain: Why You Lose Your Car Keys but Never Forget How to Drive and Other Puzzles of Everyday Life*. The book has been translated into more than 20 languages worldwide and was recipient of the AAAS/Subaru Science Book of the Year Award in the Young Adult category. He has written extensively for general audiences in *The New York Times*, *The Washington Post*, *USA Today*, and the *New York Daily News*. He speaks often to public audiences and to the media on neuroscience and on his research. He has been profiled in *The New York Times* and made appearances on National Public Radio and the TED^{x}SF and Big Think online video series.

Professor Wang lives in Princeton, New Jersey, with his wife, who is a physician; their daughter; and a pug. ■

Table of Contents

Table of Contents

Table of Contents

Table of Contents

The Neuroscience of Everyday Life

Scope:

For millennia, people have been interested in the workings of their own minds. This interest has found expression in disciplines as diverse as philosophy, medicine, and psychology. Today, neuroscience addresses the mind as arising from the brain, a biological organ. Brains mediate our daily experiences at every level, from breathing and sleeping to making decisions, loving, and learning. Neuroscience is starting to provide explanations for every aspect of behavior. Tens of thousands of neuroscientists now examine brain function at levels ranging from molecules to cells to circuits to the whole brain. Although neuroscience is often taught in terms of disease, this is an excessively limited view. We use our brains in our every action. Understanding the brain can illuminate our daily lives—and what it means to be an individual person.

The brain is an ever-changing biological organ

Popular belief has it that the brain is like a computer. The brain processes information, but beyond that, the analogy does not hold up well. Everyday experiences reveal ways in which your brain operates in a most un-computerlike fashion. Examples include visual illusions, the emotional basis of decision-making, irrational approaches to problem-solving, and the unreliability of human memory. These phenomena reflect the evolutionary history of the brain, which has been optimized by natural selection to help you live to fight another day and to reproduce. Even unusual capacities, such as humor and mathematics, are reflected by similar capacities in other animals.

A brain's entire activity consumes only about as much energy as an idling laptop. Brain cells make trillions of connections with one another. Some connections come from the external world, bringing in coded signals that drastically condense the available information. These signals are reconstituted by mechanisms in the brain—but never with absolute certainty.

The brain changes throughout life. Many changes are preprogrammed in early development, which proceeds normally except in cases of flawed genetic inheritance or severe deprivation. The interplay of genes, environment, and experience continues throughout life. From childhood to old age, active use of skills plays a major role in maintaining and enhancing function. As a biological organ, the brain is vulnerable to cardiovascular disease—and is kept healthy by physical exercise, which helps the brain retain function and can alleviate the symptoms of anxiety and depression.

A second type of change in the brain depends on experience: memory. The brain's many forms of memory each use different brain regions. The capacity to remember facts relies on the medial temporal lobe system for memory, which also handles spatial navigation; many memory tricks rely on this commonality. Memory is fluid: Information that seems to be permanently stored undergoes constant change as memories are reprocessed and consolidated, so that a decades-old memory may be vivid yet lack detail or context.

Unusual and altered states

Our brain reacts to many extreme experiences with the stress response, which temporarily conserves resources. But persistent stress can have unhealthy effects on the growth and birth of neurons. Modern life includes work, a source of chronic stress, but also play, which triggers short-term responses, such as the secretion of adrenalin, but without creating a long-term stress burden.

The brain typically represents the body in a seamless fashion, but exceptional events can occur. Pain can even be felt in an extremity after it has been amputated, a syndrome that is caused by lingering representations in the brain. Under extreme conditions, people often report incredible events, such as out-of-body and near-death experiences. Paranormal events may be caused by seizures or insult to the temporal-parietal junction, a site where body image is represented.

Humans have found ways to alter the brain's function chemically. Mind-altering drugs are as diverse as nicotine, Prozac, morphine, and caffeine. Both legal and illegal drugs work by enhancing or interfering with the function of protein molecules that process neurotransmitter signals. Receptors for a particular neurotransmitter can often be found all over the brain, leading to side effects—sometimes catastrophic ones—such as addiction.

The individual, social, and spiritual brain

Brain variations establish our individual characteristics. Some differences are small, such as those between men and women, who differ most in sexual behavior not cognitive ability. Human variation in personality and cognitive capacity is built on genetic foundations; therefore, we share many such traits with our parents. Differences in cognitive ability are also seen across generations, a period during which the environment's influence on development changes tremendously.

Humans are intensely social animals and are able to imagine the mental states of others. This capacity provides a key component for many group dynamics, including religious belief. One component of this "theory of mind" capacity may reside in the insula, which is active in processing both one's own emotional state and that of others—and perhaps provides a means for feeling sympathy for others. Insight into theory of mind may come from autism, a genetically based developmental disorder in which social reasoning is impaired.

Some areas of mental function are only beginning to be probed. One example is the basis of life happiness. Because of our ability to adapt to changing circumstances, major life events, including blindness and losing a limb, do not affect long-term happiness. Yet other life events have a lasting effect on happiness, such as gaining a life partner—or losing one. An exciting frontier is the understanding of both happiness and mood, which are profoundly affected by regions in the brain's core. These questions present a major challenge for neuroscience and its relation to everyday life. ■

What Is Neuroscience?
Lecture 1

As a working neuroscientist, I often think about such everyday experiences at two levels: One, of course, is just normal experience, trying to get the two-year-old to eat the vegetables. But, also, I think about such experiences in relation to how the brain works as a biological organ.

Fundamentally, much of this course is about everyday life, specifically, your everyday life in terms of what your brain is doing. In this course, we'll talk about our thoughts, mental health, and how we live our lives, in addition to how the brain is structured and how it works.

Neuroscience is often taught in terms of disease, but this is not the only way to look at brain function. We use our brains in our every action, whether we're aware of it or not. In this course, we will examine brain activity and the brain mechanisms underlying all sorts of everyday phenomena. We will try to understand why the brain does tricky things, some things that perhaps are not very intuitive, all in the interest of keeping us alive. We will explore explanations for how brains generate behavior and how we generate our daily experience. This course will take all of these different approaches to help us understand the brain and ourselves a little bit better. We will also look at medical disorders, but our primary focus will be on our everyday existence.

Neuroscience as a field did not exist 100 years ago. At the time, there was neurology and biology, chemistry and physics. In the last few decades, however, neuroscience has become a thriving discipline and has begun to provide mechanistic, biologically oriented explanations for every aspect of behavior—economic behavior, social behavior, and psychiatric disorders. All of these explanations discussed in the coming lectures address or affect many aspects of our lives.

Understanding the mechanics of brain function can illuminate our daily lives and what it means to be an individual person. To help with that understanding, we take a brief tour of the brain. It looks deceptively simple, like a single structure, but is composed of many regions. We'll learn about specific brain regions that seem to be involved in generating behaviors, things that we experience in our everyday lives, and break that down to biological mechanisms, such as circuits, cells, and the chemicals that neurons use to communicate. We will see how neuroscience pertains to all these mental and behavioral phenomena.

We use our brains in everything we do.

In this course, we'll talk about low levels of function and high levels of function, always in terms of everyday life. We'll also look at emotional processing and memory, an important part of our human experience and a big part of how we look at our own identity and how we think of ourselves. We'll also talk about unusual phenomena, such as out-of-body experiences and visions— paranormal phenomena.

I hope these lectures will give you a sense of what the whole brain is up to by considering all these parts together. In the next lecture, we'll look at how neuroscientists study this three-pound object, the brain. ■

Questions to Consider

1. What everyday phenomena involving mental processes have puzzled you?

2. How do you think your perception of the following fields would be altered if you understood them in terms of brain-based mechanisms: psychology, economics, political science, and moral philosophy?

How Do Neuroscientists Study the Brain?
Lecture 2

The universality of these deep principles of brain function allows us to discover principles of brain function that are shared across a wide range of organisms. What that means is that there is a hope of studying animals in order to understand human behavior and sometimes human disease.

In this lecture, we'll start to get a feeling for how neuroscientists study the brain, exactly what it is that we do, and what kinds of explanations we look for. Let's take a look at some of the ways in which neuroscientists look at the brain and at what level we explain a phenomenon.

The most basic level consists of individual molecules, which cooperate to make a single **neuron** work. Next, we have **synapses**, the connections between neurons that enable neurons to communicate with one another and send electrical signals over long distances. Groups of communicating neurons form networks, which in turn, constitute maps and systems. An entire network of brain regions talking to one another generates a behavior. The highest level is the **central nervous system**—the entire brain.

We can also look at brain function by studying the mechanisms, such as genetics, that generate changes in the brain. The environment is another factor that helps to shape who we are. Finally, neuroscientists are interested in behavior, the phenomena studied in psychology, psychiatry, sociology, and even economics. These levels of explanation are what neuroscientists look for to help us understand how the brain works.

Each level of explanation tells us something about brain function, but it doesn't necessarily tell us about a different level. We need to formulate explanations that join these different levels of analysis, just like joining molecules to synapses to neurons to circuits.

Neuroscientists use the scientific method in pursuing a general framework in which these different levels of explanation can start to connect to help us understand the brain. With the scientific method, any idea is provisional: If an experiment yields evidence that contradicts the idea, the idea is rejected. The scientific method also requires that levels of explanation connect with one another.

To test an idea, neuroscientists use a three-part process to design an experiment. First, they decide which brain region to test. Next, they form a hypothesis suggested by existing evidence. Finally, they consider technology issues. Technology limits what we are able to do in an experiment.

Two commonly held beliefs lose credibility when viewed from a neuroscientific perspective and in light of existing evidence. The first is that alcohol kills neurons, and the second is that classical music makes babies smarter (the Mozart effect).

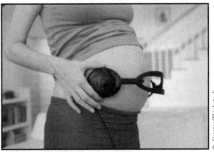

Postmortem exams revealed that alcoholics' brains were smaller than normal, suggesting that, because brains are made up of neuron cells, alcohol must be killing neurons. But studies showed that cells got smaller, not fewer in number. Heavy drinkers can, however, develop

The myth that playing classical music to a fetus makes for a smarter baby has been refuted.

Wernicke-Korsakoff syndrome, in which drinking leads to loss of brain cells by creating a thiamine deficiency that kills neurons.

Belief in the so-called Mozart effect originated in a technical report in *Nature*, a leading international science journal. Researchers found that playing classical music to a group made them somewhat better in one of a set of intelligence tests. However, the test subjects were college students, not babies, and the effect lasted only 20 minutes. The original result was not reproducible and has been refuted. In related findings, children who learned to play a musical instrument seemed to be better at spatial reasoning tasks.

When neuroscientists do find a large framework of explanation for how the brain works, with ideas at different levels that connect to one another, we call these frameworks theories. Developing theories is the long-term goal of neuroscience. ■

Important Terms

central nervous system (CNS): The part of the nervous system comprising the brain and spinal cord.

neuron: Specialized cells of the nervous system.

synapse: Specialized contact between 2 neurons that allows one to send signals to the other.

Questions to Consider

1. In the case of a major brain-based disorder, such as Alzheimer's disease or autism, what level of explanation for its causes would you find satisfactory?

2. Think of a popular belief about the brain that you have taken for granted but wonder if it's really true. Example: You use only 10 percent of your brain.

Evolution, Energetics, and the 10% Myth
Lecture 3

> The brain is not like a computer. ... [It] really is a survival machine. It helps you live to fight another day. It's not there performing some kind of supercomputing operation and leading to some calculation of pi to 100 digits.

If you called someone a rat, you could always explain that animals and humans have many features in common, from molecules all the way up to the way our brains are laid out and the way they function. The similarity between us and animals—both in cellular structures and behaviors—enables us to study brain function in non-human animals, a recurring theme in the study of neuroscience that we will discuss further in this lecture.

The universal similarities between brains across the animal kingdom, especially related species, are evident when comparing, for example, a rat brain and a human brain. These brains look fairly similar, both to an untrained eye and to a neuroscientist.

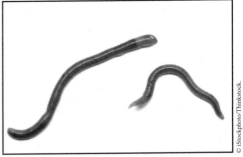

The nervous system of a small worm has a few hundred neurons, compared to hundreds of billions in a human.

The structures in the brains are arranged in similar relationships to one another. The thing that's different is the size or the relative proportion of these structures. It's a question of differences of degree as opposed to some qualitative difference in the basic brain plan.

Another kind of similarity can be found at the cellular level. Nervous systems throughout the animal kingdom are made of neurons and, in many cases, **glial cells**. These two cell types have analogous physiological functions that are the universal currency of brain signaling. Life is similar at the molecular level, illustrating what's known as the principle of common descent, or the idea that these signaling molecules are the same because they had a similar ancestor. That similar ancestor is seen in diverse animal life.

Plenty of dissimilarities also exist, of course. **Proteins** aren't identical, **genes** are regulated differently, and differing brain sizes—and the proportions of different brain components—mean that larger brains have more neurons and are more complex.

Some general principles arising from animal work have led to two popular misconceptions about the brain, namely, that it is like a computer and that we use only about 10% of our brains.

Your brain is not like a computer. It's well laid out and energy efficient, but it's really a survival machine that has been optimized over millions of generations of **natural selection** and **evolution** to help you survive—even lying to you when necessary in the interest of keeping you alive. That's a central principle of how brains are organized.

The second misconception, the 10% myth, is prevalent worldwide and has cultural consequences. It's used to motivate us to work harder and to explain paranormal phenomena. The pioneering psychologist and pre-neuroscientist William James gave public lectures in the early 20th century in which he told audiences that we reach only a small fraction of our brain's full potential. The **mutation** to 10% came from a nonscientist, self-help guru Dale Carnegie, as a way to boost book sales.

We know that we need all of our brain to function and that a lot of brain activity is occurring even when we are focused on one task. Monitoring brain activity with fMRI or PET scanners and studying damaged brains to observe what functions are lost or affected show that every part of the brain is essential. It's possible to localize different brain regions to be necessary for various kinds of functions based on lesion and brain injury data, but in general, we require 100% of our brains. ■

evolution: When referring to biological systems specifically, a change in allele frequencies over time in a genetically continuous population of organisms.

gene: A stretch of DNA that designates the construction of one protein.

glial cells: An accessory type of cell found in the nervous system.

mutation: An error in the copying of a gene.

natural selection: The process by which competition for limited resources causes the preservation or elimination of particular alleles.

protein: One of 5 categories of organic molecules present in all organisms. A protein consists of a chain of amino acids, the sequence of which is determined by information encoded in the genome.

Questions to Consider

1. Why would it be useful for blood flow to increase in response to brain activity?

2. What does the case of Phineas Gage tell us about whether different parts of the brain have specialized roles in determining who we are?

Neurons and Synapses
Lecture 4

> By cutting the brain in half, what ended up happening was that the left half of the brain and the right half of the brain were no longer able to communicate. … What those surgeons generated was two people for the price of one—two halves of the brain not communicating with one another.

We say that the brain uses 15 watts of electricity, but what's that 15 watts of power buying us? The answer is that the 15 watts of power is used to drive an elaborate chemical mechanism that generates the signals of the brain. In this lecture, we'll talk about how those signals are made.

The brain generates electrical signals, but the brain is fundamentally chemical in nature. Electrical signals of the brain are directly generated by chemicals called ions. Cells move ions around, and this movement helps to generate electrical signals. Chemicals are also used as signaling molecules to send information from one neuron to another (synaptic transmission) and to send information inside cells. Neurons release and detect chemicals to communicate with each other and to generate chemicals inside the cell. These signals can be used to process and store information and generate changes that can last for a second or a lifetime.

Neurons use an output structure called an **axon** to send signals and use input structures called **dendrites** to receive information transmitted across the synapse. The synaptic inputs generate an electrical response that the cell body receives and turns into signals that go out again.

The neuron is like a bag of salts surrounded by membranes, made of fat, that are studded with proteins. These proteins allow ions to move back and forth across the membrane, generating electrical currents. These proteins also come in multiple categories. One category encompasses ion pumps, which set the stage for electrical signaling by moving ions across the membrane and creating concentration gradients. Another category consists of **ion**

channels—little bridges that allow ions to cross passively. That passive opening is a key component of generating electrical signals in the brain from moment to moment.

A critical component of signaling in the brain is the **action potential**, the spike. In such an event, an all-or-nothing signal composed of sodium enters the cell and potassium exits the cell. The other major component of electrical signaling in brains is synaptic transmission, which involves other ion channels that are sensitive to **neurotransmitters**. These neurotransmitter-gated ion channels—ion channels that are opened by neurotransmitters—are how neurons communicate with one another.

The neurons make up a superhighway of connections between the left half and the right half of the brain. When this pathway is cut, the halves of the brain can't communicate with each other. This is how it was discovered that the halves of the brain—the left half of the brain and the right half of the brain—each have their own general abilities and specialized jobs. When neurosurgeons cut patients' brains at the midline to prevent seizures, the halves of the brain could no longer communicate because the axons were

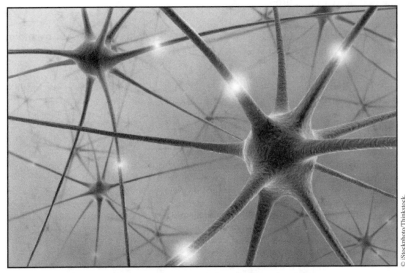

Neurons receive chemical signals via their branch-like dendrites.

cut. In essence, the surgeons had generated two people for the price of one because of this operation.

Neurotransmitters have other functions besides just opening ion channels, and there are other receptors that play a critical role in neural signaling. These other receptors for neurotransmitters are enzymes, not ion channels. That turns out to be a major part of what brains do. It is how drugs and other chemicals work in the brain, a subject we will turn to in the next lecture. ■

Important Terms

action potential: A change in membrane potential arising at the axon hillock; it travels down the axon in an all-or-none fashion.

axon: The process of a neuron specialized for the transmission of information; axons are the physical structures that connect different areas of the brain.

dendrite: The part of the neuron that receives signals from other neurons. Dendrites tend to come in the form of highly branched cables coming from the cell body of a neuron.

ion channel: Generally a protein that regulates the flow of ions, for example, across a membrane.

neurotransmitter: Small molecules used by the brain to transmit signals across synapses from one neuron to another.

Questions to Consider

1. During which part of an action potential do sodium ions flow across the neuron membrane? Potassium ions?

2. What is the role of axons in integrating the functions of the left half and right half of the brain?

Neurotransmitters and Drugs
Lecture 5

There's some concern about glutamate in the form of MSG causing headaches and bad health reactions. ...our brains have grams and grams of glutamate. Each one of our neurons secretes buckets of glutamate. Our heads are basically filled with glutamate.

Although the brain uses electrical activity—efficiently running the show on only 15 watts of power—it depends on a careful orchestration of chemical reactions to help generate and influence that activity. In this lecture, we'll look at that brain chemistry.

Neurotransmission is how neurons communicate. Electrical synapses are direct connections between neurons, but the most common means of communication is chemical communication using neurotransmitters. A neuron secretes chemicals called neurotransmitters that cross tiny gaps, called synapses, to act on **receptors**. Receptors are protein molecules that sit in the membrane of the cell. They bind to neurotransmitters, causing a shape change in the receptor. That change is a fundamental step underlying nearly all communication in the brain.

Camillo Golgi, one of the pioneers of neuroscience.

About 90% of neurons (glutamatergic) secrete **glutamate**, an **amino acid** that can cause excitation; almost 10% of neurons (GABAergic) secrete **GABA (gamma-aminobutyric acid)**, the main inhibitory neurotransmitter of the brain, or glycine; and the remaining neurons have metabotropic receptors, which drive metabolism. A neuron cannot secrete both glutamate and GABA.

The main receptors in the brain for processing many electrical signals are receptors for glutamate, GABA, and glycine. These are ion channels. The metabotropic receptors receive neurotransmitters from molecules (**biogenic amines**) that include **dopamine**, **norepinephrine**, and **serotonin**. Other small molecules that mostly work through metabotropic receptors are histamine and peptides.

Some of the most influential chemicals in our body are produced by a tiny fraction of neurons. For example, of the 50 to 100 billion neurons in the human brain, only 200,000 secrete dopamine, yet dopamine plays a wide variety of critical roles in brain function.

We often refer to the neurotransmitter as a ligand, a technical term for the molecule that binds to the receptor. This concept of a ligand is important because the ligand is not only a neurotransmitter, but it can be other molecules, as well. Some of these, in fact, are drugs that can be taken to affect brain function.

> **Some of the most influential chemicals in our body are produced by a tiny fraction of neurons.**

To get an idea of how much of this action is packed into our brain, imagine a cubic centimeter—about a thimbleful. This tiny amount of tissue contains all the things we've discussed so far in this course—neurons, axons, dendrites, and synapses. One cubic centimeter of tissue contains about 50 million neurons, several hundred miles of axons, and several hundred miles of dendrites. In the same cubic centimeter of tissue, you have a trillion synaptic connections.

One of the mysteries in neuroscience is the unreliability of most synapses, the gaps that neurotransmitters must cross for neurons to communicate with each other. Typically anywhere between one and four times out of five, nothing is released. Synapses are so weak that it takes around 100 all firing together to get a postsynaptic neuron to fire an action potential. Synapses are so small as to be unreliable, but simultaneous firing and packing a trillion of them into a thimbleful seems to work well. Some synapses in the brain and nervous systems are very reliable, such as at the neuromuscular junction, which controls muscle contraction.

Computer simulations and direct measurement of brain activity imply that synaptic signaling consumes a lot of energy. Although individual synapses are not terribly reliable, in the aggregate, they use much of the brain's energy. ■

Important Terms

amino acids: The building blocks of proteins; about 20 different kinds, akin to letters, exist.

biogenic amines: In the context of how the term is used in this course, it refers to the monoamine neurotransmitters dopamine, norepinephrine, and serotonin.

dopamine: A neurotransmitter whose functions include a role in sequential thought (such that abnormal dopamine levels are associated with the disordered thought of schizophrenia), the anticipation of pleasure, and aspects of fine motor control.

gamma-aminobutyric acid (GABA): A major inhibitory neurotransmitter of the CNS, particularly of interneurons.

glutamate: An excitatory neurotransmitter with critical roles in learning and memory. An excess of glutamate induces *excitotoxicity*, a route by which neurons are killed during various neurological insults.

norepinephrine (a.k.a. noradrenaline): A neurotransmitter whose functions include release from the ends of the final neurons in the sympathetic nervous system, as well as a role in depression (with, most likely, a depletion occurring).

serotonin: A neurotransmitter whose functions include a role in aggression, sleep onset, depression, and impulsivity.

1. What are the similarities and differences between drugs compared with our brain's own neurotransmitters?

2. Based on the last two lectures, list ways in which your brain differs from a computer: for example, power usage, reliability of components, and fundamental principle of generating electrical signal.

Juicing the Brain
Lecture 6

There are other drugs that we take in daily life that lead to dependency because they cause plastic events of the brain. These lead us to require those substances ... daily. ... A familiar example is caffeine. Caffeine leads to a dependency. ... We have a certain level of caffeine that we come to expect on a daily basis.

When we have a chemical imbalance or if we seek to alter our own chemical responses in some way, we sometimes seek a remedy in therapeutic chemicals—drugs. These drugs do many of the same things as naturally occurring neurotransmitters. Drugs can imitate neurotransmitters or modify what neurotransmitters do, even block neurotransmitter action. But they can also have deep, lasting, and profound effects on brain function.

Cognitive enhancers, taken to improve mental functions, and other mind-altering drugs alter a neuron's ability to release neurotransmitters and alter how a neuron receives neurotransmitters. A chemical can activate the receptor, or it can bind to the receptor and not activate it, preventing other chemicals from getting in. Once a neuron releases a neurotransmitter, it is eventually vacuumed back into the cells (reuptake) or it's broken down. Some drugs block the reuptake of neurotransmitters.

In most cases, drugs work on signaling pathways connected to biochemical signaling inside neurons. The oldest drugs in use today are caffeine and nicotine, benchmarks to which other performance-enhancing drugs are compared.

Let's consider how caffeine and marijuana affect us on a molecular level. Caffeine blocks receptors for adenosine, an inhibitory neurotransmitter that acts as a brake and is believed to help promote sleep. Another kind of receptor that acts like a brake is the cannabinoid receptor, activated by chemicals made in the brain called endocannabinoids. The chemical in marijuana that makes you high is delta-9-TCH, and it puts a foot on the brake and suppresses the release of a neurotransmitter. Again, caffeine takes a foot off the brake through adenosine receptors, and delta-9-THC puts a foot on the brake. In some sense, marijuana is the anticaffeine. Although not exact opposites, these drugs affect the brain in opposite ways.

Some drugs affect dopamine signaling. Dopamine, as well as serotonin, adrenalin (also called **epinephrine**), and histamine, are neurotransmitters involved in regulating mood, learning, movement, and basic physiological responses. Dopamine is involved in decision making (executive function), reward, personality, and the regulation of movement. When dopamine neurons die, one result is **Parkinson's disease**; another can be schizophrenia.

Dopamine uptake blockers that affect dopamine function can lead to addiction. These drugs, including amphetamines and cocaine, cause the dopamine (which seems to convey a sense of reward) to linger in the synapse

Nicotine use leads to dependency because it causes plastic events of the brain.

and neural tissue. The brain can then adapt to that overstimulation. Another drug in this category that may be addictive is Ritalin, given to children to address attention deficit hyperactive disorder, or ADHD. The benchmark for addiction is amphetamine, which is mostly—not entirely—irreversible.

There are other drugs that we take in daily life that lead to dependency because they cause plastic events of the brain. These lead us to require those substances daily. A familiar example is caffeine; another is nicotine.

Nicotine binds to receptors for **acetylcholine**, activates receptors that can alter the sensitivity of neurons to input, and alters long-term learning mechanisms. Besides being addictive and habit forming, nicotinic receptor activation can enhance brain function. Some drugs that reduce the symptoms of **Alzheimer's disease** enhance neuronal function by acting on nicotinic acetylcholine receptors.

Drugs do many of the same things as naturally occurring neurotransmitters, but the effects of drugs are typically enhanced compared to the effects of native neurotransmitters. Drugs can lead to unnatural highs and unnaturally block the action of neurotransmitters. In many cases, the outcome of taking drugs is to enhance function, but there is also a risk of causing long-term changes in the brain. ■

Important Terms

acetylcholine: A neurotransmitter whose functions include release from the ends of the final neurons in the parasympathetic nervous system.

Alzheimer's disease: A degenerative neurological disorder characterized primarily by the loss of neurons in higher-order regions of the neocortex, limbic system structures, and specific reticular formation nuclei with widespread projections to the cortex.

cognitive/cognition: Related to mental activities such as thinking, learning, and memory.

epinephrine (a.k.a. adrenaline): Both a neurotransmitter throughout the brain and a hormone released in the adrenal gland during stress as a result of activation of the sympathetic nervous system.

Parkinson's disease: A neurodegenerative disease resulting from the loss of neurons in the substantia nigra of the midbrain; characterized by a resting tremor, abnormal posture, and paucity of normal movement.

1. What characteristics would make a drug unsuitable for everyday use? Should some currently legal drugs, such as Adderall, be regulated more stringently, and why?

2. Dopamine neurons project axons to many different locations. How could this relate to dopamine's diverse contributions to brain function?

Coming to Your Senses
Lecture 7

The job of receptor cells—receptor cells are cells in the periphery of our nervous system, our skin, eyes, and ears—is converting events in the world to spikes. Spikes are this universal currency of brain information."

None of the trillions of connections that neurons make with one another can give us direct information about the external world. The brain lacks touch receptors, instead relying on millions of axonal wires that come into the brain from the world to provide **sensation**. We must use the neutral, decoded information and make inferences based on our lifetime of experience.

Our senses—touch, smell, taste, hearing, and sight—use specific receptor cells to convert events from the world into an electrical current or to a chemical signaling, which is then converted to a signal in a neuron, then to a spike, which travels to the brain. Sensation works differently for different senses, and all the senses have different kinds of receptor cells. The specific properties of receptor cells determine what the spikes encode. However, every sense follows the general principle of converting stimuli into spikes.

Skin has many different kinds of touch receptors, each sensitive to pain, temperature, food chemicals (such as capsaicin in hot peppers), pressure changes, or vibration. The heat receptors convert temperature to an electrical signal. Some nerve endings are open ended, their axons terminating in the skin. Other mechanical structures in the skin have sheathed nerve endings and sense pressure changes and vibration.

Hearing is also sensitive to vibrations; with this sense, vibrations are converted into spikes. In this case, the sensor cells are in the **cochlea** in the inner ear. Hair cells are the primary sensor cells. Vibrations in the hair cells trigger secretion of a neurotransmitter. Then, the target neurons, the **ganglion** cells, fire spikes that are transmitted along the auditory nerve into the brain.

These hair cell receptors can be damaged or killed by loud music and opiate drugs, but silicon cochlea have been implanted successfully worldwide to restore hearing.

Chemical senses allow us to taste and smell. Together, they make flavors. Our tongue has nerve endings with receptors for chemicals. These receptors react to sweet, sour, salty, bitter, and umami, a Japanese term meaning, generally, delicious. We have an innate liking for sweet, salty, and umami, but we have more taste receptors for bitter because it is important for survival to detect bitter compounds, which are often poisonous.

Skin has many different kinds of touch receptors, each sensitive to pain, temperature, food chemicals (such as capsaicin in hot peppers), pressure changes, or vibration.

Smell is critical to the sense of flavor and is seamlessly integrated with taste. We have hundreds of different kinds of odorant receptors, giving us quite a sophisticated ability to detect smells. But despite our innate preferences for certain tastes, we have no natural preference for smells or flavors and must learn them.

The most complex sense is vision, which is really multiple senses bound up in one. It's the sense of vision that is processed by major parts of the brain—approximately 40% of the neocortex and other brain regions.

Like the other senses, vision begins with receptor cells, but these are sensitive to light—some to dim light, others to color. These signals are converted to chemical and then to electrical signals that are sent to multiple locations in the brain that do different things. These pathways are, to some extent, independent from each other. This is why damage to specific regions of the brain can affect some aspects of vision, such as loss of color, motion, or form, without causing total blindness. For example, if the optic tectum is fine, but the visual cortex is damaged, you would be able to catch a ball and navigate through an obstacle course—but be convinced that you were completely blind. ∎

cochlea: Fluid-filled structure of the inner ear.

ganglion (pl. ganglia): A group of cell bodies in the peripheral nervous system; comparable to a nucleus in the central nervous system.

sensation: The result of stimulation of sense organs; can also be a "feeling" in the somatosensory system.

Questions to Consider

1. What is the common signaling event into which all external information from the world must be translated before your brain can understand it?

2. What does blind sight tell us about the organization of the visual system?

Perception and Your Brain's Little Lies
Lecture 8

> Perception depends on attention and expectations—for instance, what you're expecting to get. ... Perception also depends on a lifetime of prior experience.

Our senses bombard us with information, but how do we know what to make of it all? You may think that you can trust your eyes, your hearing, or what you're touching, but it may surprise you to learn that your brain is probably lying to you and lies to you most of the time.

The brain must interpret the sensations flooding in from all over the body, and it begins by filtering information and discarding much of it. Our brain looks for novelty, then adapts and ignores that sensation while it attends to something else. Perceived sensations depend on context to help us determine whether something is a good or bad event or whether something is important or not important. The brain infers the most likely primary event that happened based on prior assumptions about what should happen and what is expected.

Sensations are routed to different parts of the brain in a touch map that represents those parts of the sensory world that are most important to us. This map is called a **homunculus** (Latin for "little human being"). For example, more of the map represents the face, lips, and hands than, say, the trunk. Often, senses have more than one representation. This principle of a map extends to multiple maps for multiple functions even for one system. For example, vision consists of multiple things, features that are extracted—color, pattern, and motion.

The primary visual cortex is a map of our visual world with separate pathways that interpret input in different ways, such as spatial orientation, motion, and color. Scientists also refer to the "what" (form) and "where" (motion) pathways. Despite its sophisticated mapping and filtering, however, it's possible to trick the brain into interpreting these pathways differently with optical illusions. Optical illusions, in general, and other illusions, too, take advantage of the complexity of the system. The general principle is that the multiplicity of visual pathways can be fooled by cleverly designed visual stimuli to give you a feeling of an optical illusion.

Our brain throws away familiar information, beginning immediately in the touch receptors. It's a phenomenon called adaptation, which allows us to ignore the feel of our clothes while we focus on a novel sensation—say, the temperature of the coffee we're about to sip. Already at the very first stages, familiar information has begun to be thrown away, with the separation of ongoing stimulation from new stimulation.

Our expectations also influence the sensory responses in receptors and influence our **perceptions**. The perception of the body's sensations comes from the interaction of two processes: (1) signals coming from receptors in your body and activity in brain pathways that control your response to these signals and (2) the gating of the information, including whether the information gets passed along at all. For example, we cannot tickle ourselves.

Besides integrating information from one sense, we also unknowingly integrate multiple senses to interpret events. For instance, it's possible to influence our auditory perceptions based on visual input. Watch a video of a woman saying "dah dah" matched with audio of her saying "bah bah." The inferences made by your brain will cause you to hear something like "the the." Listen to the audio with your eyes closed, and you hear "bah bah." It's an example of the brain using visual cues to determine what was probably said and interpreting what was probably being said, part of the reason why it's easier to understand a conversation in person than over the telephone. ∎

Important Terms

homunculus: Distorted figure of a "man" mapped onto brain regions in motor and somatosensory areas.

perception: The mental process or act of awareness of an object or idea.

1. The brain is filled with maps, for instance, of the visual world or of the body surface. How do you imagine a map for sound or smell would be organized?

2. Explain why the stepping-feet illusion works. Would it work if it were done entirely in black and white?

Pain—All in Your Head?
Lecture 9

In a sense, as I've described, pain is all in your head—as the saying goes. ... Pain is a perception that's generated entirely within the brain. ... It's very real and it's something that helps us survive. But it is something that's generated within the brain.

All of our perceptions come from inferences the brain makes from the myriad bits of information it receives, deciding which bits to ignore and which bits to use, but the perceptions are very real. In this lecture, we'll discuss the perception of pain, which begins as signals from receptors but goes through a different processing than other sensations.

Signals travel up the spinal cord to the **thalamus**, where all sensory information goes on its way into the brain. Other brain regions for perception and judgment of pain include the somatosensory cortex, the insula, and the anterior cingulate cortex. These regions are activated by

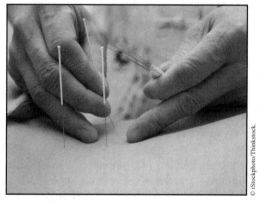
Acupuncture has proven effective at treating chronic pain and nausea.

different kinds of pain: They judge the emotional content of pain, where it hurts, and whether we feel guilt or disgust; they are also activated when we see someone else in pain. Our conscious behavior is seated in the anterior cingulated cortex, which integrates cognition and selecting responses.

Referred pain is when your brain confuses the source of pain. For example, pain in your arm could indicate a heart attack, and pain in your shoulder may indicate a problem in your liver or diaphragm.

Depending on context, the brain can perceive pain differently. A soldier wounded in battle needs a lower dose of painkillers during field surgery than a civilian would require for the same kind of surgery in a hospital back home.

Brain scans show that yogi masters can control pain by controlling activity in brain regions known to be involved in pain. Despite being subjected to painful stimuli, there is nearly no activation of the insular cortex and no perception of pain. For the rest of us, however, there are drugs and other methods of easing or eliminating pain.

The two classes of painkillers are prostaglandin blockers and opiates. Prostaglandin blockers include aspirin, ibuprofen, and acetaminophen (Tylenol). These are all drugs that seem to act peripherally. That is, they act on pain reception mechanisms, and they all seem to block second messenger synthesis. Opiates—which include morphine, codeine, and heroin—are drugs that act on receptors for opiates. Such receptors are present throughout the nervous system, spinal cord, and brain—even in the hair cells of your ear and in your gut. That's why opiate use can lead to undesirable side effects, such as constipation or hearing loss. We don't know exactly how opiates work. Combining the two types of drugs, such as ibuprofen and codeine, is very effective.

Other painkillers are the brain's own naturally secreted opiates, called **opioids**, or endorphins. Another type of pain relief may be provided by the placebo effect, in which patients are told they are receiving a medication when they are really being given dummy pills—but there is some evidence that this triggers a very real secretion of endorphins or opioids in the brain. Neurosurgery is a desperate measure for pain relief, because it involves cutting or removing parts of the brain. However, newer methods include electrically activating certain brain regions to activate or deactivate the regions, giving some degree of pain relief without killing brain tissue.

A nonmedical approach to pain treatment is acupuncture. It has no clear basis in Western medicine, and it has been ineffective for treating most medical problems (such as cancer or organ problems). However, in control trials, acupuncture works better than control treatments for treating chronic pain and nausea. ■

Questions to Consider

1. How does the maps-in-the-brain concept help account for phantom limb syndrome?

2. How does the brain's way of processing pain affect what we can do to treat pain in the future?

Decisions—Your Brain's Secret Ballot
Lecture 10

> Usually when we think about emotions and decisions, we say emotions interfere with our ability to make sensible choices. ... But that's not right. Emotions (we're not talking about moods)—these immediate responses that we have—occur in response to events in the world. Emotions keep our brains focused on critical information.

I f you're still weighing the evidence while you decide whether to take that other job yet or are still determining which candidate will get your vote, maybe you just aren't yet aware of the decision that's probably already set in your mind.

Decisions in our lives involve two categories commonly referred to as cognitive, the integration and careful weighing of evidence, and affective (emotional), the determination of whether an outcome will be good or bad. In all cases, decisions seem to contain multiple components. They include integrating information, committing to a choice, and acting. Of all the things that are happening to us, which are the things that we need to pay attention to that are really important? This concept of value is determined by the brain's emotional systems.

Emotions keep our brains focused on critical information and motivate us to shape our behavior to gain what we desire and to avoid what we fear. In most cases, you only have your intuition to go on. You need an emotional factor in decision-making to appreciate possible outcomes of a decision.

Three areas of the brain (the amygdala, anterior cingulated cortex, and **orbitofrontal cortex**) are involved in processing emotions. Damage to these areas can be disastrous. Affected people find it difficult to make even minor decisions; they aren't embarrassed by socially inappropriate behavior; they are unable to respond appropriately to negative events; they can't anticipate the probable consequences of their actions; and they can't make sensible choices.

Cognitive decision-making involves considering imperfect information and making a decision as quickly as possible. There is a tradeoff between accuracy and speed in gathering value and trying to make a decision quickly. Psychologists have studied an axis of decision-making that has maximizers on one end and satisficers on the other. Maximizers demand the best outcome and spend a lot of time worrying about differences, no matter how small. Satisficers, a term coined by political scientist Herb Simon to combine "satisfy" and "suffice," look until they find something good enough, then stop. They are decisive and don't look back. Maximizers are focused on accuracy and are trying to get as close to the ideal right answer as possible. Satisficers focus on speed. On average, satisficers are happier than maximizers.

Cognitive decision making involves considering imperfect information and making a decision as quickly as possible.

Scientists studying decision-making on a cellular level have found that the parietal cortex is a region that seems to accumulate evidence the way that we accumulate evidence during a task. Groups of neurons work together to integrate information, accumulating information until some threshold is reached and a decision is made. Neuroscientists don't know whether this threshold in the parietal cortex is the final choice—whether that brain region drives the final choice—or whether there's some other structure deeper in the brain that drives the choice. But it's brain activity that corresponds to the collecting of evidence.

Awareness of a decision can come much later than the commitment. We can be committed to a decision and not be aware of it. We are often unaware of our internal commitment to a choice. The commitment is made, but we don't know about it yet. ■

Important Terms

emotion: A basic, physiological state characterized by identifiable autonomic or bodily changes.

orbitofrontal cortex: A part of the frontal lobe involved in impulse control, inculcation of cultural mores, and ability to appreciate the consequences of one's behavior.

Questions to Consider

1. What is the difference between cognitively based and emotionally based decision-making? Are these processes ever combined in everyday life?

2. What is the cost of a maximizer approach to decision-making? Are you a maximizer or a satisficer?

Reward, Adaptation, and Addiction
Lecture 11

The brain changes in response to experience. ... Our brains learn and change in response to a changing world. In the case of dopamine, this ability to adapt is mostly very useful, but it turns out to be un-useful in a very important way. It leads to ... addiction.

Throughout our day, we evaluate what merits our attention and what we can afford to ignore. But how do we decide what is valuable? A basic component of how we assign value to daily events is a concept that neuroscientists call reward, defined as an event that makes you more likely to repeat the behavior that led to the reward.

The neurotransmitter dopamine is essential in conveying reward. Reward neurons, which trigger dopamine, are found in multiple parts of the brain (the orbitofrontal cortex, striatum, and amygdala). They differ from sensory neurons because reward neurons respond to the rewarding aspect as opposed to some literal aspect of a stimulus, such as taste. They stop firing when you no longer want the reward, as when you no longer want another bite of chocolate. Reward and emotional decision-making are closely linked because they share common brain areas and help people choose behaviors that lead to positive outcomes.

Such drugs as heroin, morphine, nicotine, cocaine, and amphetamine block the normal uptake, or disposal, of dopamine after the neurons have used it. These lingering neurotransmitters force the brain to adapt to a higher average level of dopamine. In turn, the brain produces fewer dopamine receptors (a phenomenon called receptor downregulation) in response to this increased level, an adaptation that makes normal pleasures, such as food, sex, and social interactions, seem less satisfying. The amount of dopamine that is generated from drug abuse is greater than what would typically happen through any normal event

The brain associates the reward, or elevated dopamine level, with the drug, so that even anticipation, such as handling drug paraphernalia, can increase the addict's drug craving. These addictive drugs push the reward mechanisms way out of range, which seems to be a critical part of generating the craving. In animal experiments, animals starved to death when forced to choose between food and artificial stimulation of their brain regions involved in addiction formation.

Physicians use the CAGE test to look for troublesome traits pointing to addiction, such as alcohol abuse. C is for cut back: Have you ever tried to cut back on your use? A is for annoyed: Are loved ones ever annoyed by your use? G is for guilt: Do you ever feel guilty about your level of use? E is for eye-opener: Do you ever need an eye-opener, such as a drink when you first wake up?

> **Physicians use the CAGE test to look for troublesome traits pointing to addiction, such as alcohol abuse.**

Before we rush to label a time-consuming interest or habit an addiction, however, we should note the differences between the natural and artificial stimuli. One major difference is how intensely the dopaminergic system is activated. Normal levels of reward don't involve addictive mechanisms or withdrawal. Normal social rewards that we experience in everyday life do not involve whole-cell rewiring and reconfiguring of brain circuits. Normal levels of reward don't induce us to abandon other daily pleasures. ∎

Questions to Consider

1. In cocaine and amphetamine addiction, how do the adaptive properties of dopamine receptors account for the need for more of the drug and for reduced pleasure in everyday activities?

2. Is there an everyday activity for which you would fail the CAGE test? Based on the lecture, are you concerned about addiction?

The Many Forms of Memory
Lecture 12

> There was a very interesting study done around 2001 in which [London] taxi drivers' brains were imaged. ... What was found was that over time, with more and more months of experience—up to 10 years of experience, 30 years of experience—that there was a shift in their hippocampal structure. ... What this suggests is the possibility that years of practice led to rewiring, led to changes, growth, retraction in the hippocampus.

When we forget where we left the car keys, we don't suddenly wonder if we'll still remember how to drive the car. We know that memory is a complex function relying on many regions of the brain, multiple memory systems where experience can rewire and restructure some of the brain regions involved in memory.

We think of memory as being declarative or nondeclarative; declarative memory is the ability to recite facts and events, such as recalling that London is the capital of England. Nondeclarative memory includes recalling how to do a certain skill, such as play the cello. Regions for this kind of memory include the cerebellum.

Neuroscientists once believed that memory was a widespread function, that some kind of general head injury could diminish all functions, including memory. But the famous case of Henry Molaison revealed that damage to a particular part of the brain affects memory in different ways. In the 1950s, this 27-year-old man had such debilitating epileptic seizures that a neurosurgeon removed a portion of his **hippocampus** (a brain region that seems to be important in the storage of facts and events) and some surrounding brain structures. This radical experimental procedure all but eliminated the seizures but left Molaison unable to form new memories (anterograde amnesia) and unable to recall memories from several years before the surgery (retrograde amnesia).

Declarative memory relies on the medial temporal lobe. This memory system includes the hippocampus and structures that surround the hippocampus in the medial temporal cortex, a major part of the brain that is involved in memory storage. All these brain regions work together and store new facts and new events. Molaison's memory loss seems to indicate that memories might be initially stored in the hippocampus, then transferred to another brain region and consolidated. Neuroscientists believe that memories are rewritten and reinforced as we re-experience them; thus, the playback of memories may be important in strengthening them. It's also believed that rewriting can lead to eventual transfer of information from one brain region to another.

The hippocampus is good at remembering events in context, such as recalling eating a picnic under a tree.

Spatial navigation also relies on the hippocampus, perhaps an ancestral function supplemented by declarative and nondeclarative functions during the course of human evolution. Brain scans in a 2001 study showed that London taxi drivers with many years of experience navigating that city's streets had changes in volume in the anterior and posterior regions of the hippocampus.

The hippocampus is good at remembering events in context, such as recalling eating a picnic under a tree. Navigating in a spatial environment is also an event in a context. In memory consolidation, events seem to be separated from the context in which they occur, resulting in something called a "gist memory," such as a memory of a parent kissing your cheek as a child.

Memories can get recalled and rewritten, but suggestions of memories can be stored and recalled as events that really happened. This rewriting process to form false memory is called repressed memory. ■

hippocampus: A brain region within the limbic system that plays a central role in learning and memory.

Questions to Consider

1. What does the case of Henry Molaison tell us about how memories of events in our lives might be stored in the short term and the long term?

2. What brain regions do navigation and declarative memory have in common?

Quirks of Memory
Lecture 13

> People are biased in the way they assimilate information; is there a way we can get people to be more objective? ... There is one trick ... that appears to work in counteracting false belief formation. Let's just call that cure "considering the opposite."... It pays for consumers of controversial news to take a moment and consider that the opposite interpretation may be true.

They say you can't trust anyone, and we know that even our own brains lie to us. The brain filters stimuli according to our experience and expectations, sometimes even altering memories as they are recalled, reprocessed, and stored again. Despite their imperfections, however, our many memory systems are well suited for their original functions—helping us to survive—even if they lead to quirks and unwanted phenomena.

Three regions of the brain involved in learning—that is, acquiring memory—are the hippocampus, the **amygdala**, and the neocortex. The hippocampus deals with spatial navigation, or learning how to get around in a complex environment. This structure requires repetition to assimilate information. For the amygdala, recruited to process intense emotions, it takes only a single trial to learn fear conditioning. The largest region, the neocortex, occupies three-quarters of the brain and generalizes factual information, storing it in a distributive way.

The ancient Greeks and Romans used a memory trick called memory palaces, still used today, to remember a large, complex body of information; the trick involves imagining navigation of a complex environment to learn long lists of facts. This technique uses our brain's natural tendency to navigate complex spatial environments, where all the landmarks and cues help us get through some path that we are trying to learn.

Biologically prepared learning is another type of learning that comes naturally to us because it reflects events that happen to us frequently—such as avoiding certain foods that have made you sick.

Our ability to learn from a single intensely emotional experience can lead to the unwelcome phenomenon of **post-traumatic stress disorder** (PTSD), induced by a traumatic event that can trigger profound changes in the brain. Treatment can use quirks of memory to help unlearn the association of the environment with the trauma; drugs can also be used to block learning mechanisms immediately after the traumatic experience to prevent the fear memory from being consolidated and transferred to long-term memory.

These multiple memory systems, some requiring one trial and others requiring many trials, sometimes transferring an experience to long-term memory and sometimes not, might offer a mechanism-based explanation of phobias. For example, declarative memory, memory for facts and places and episodes, forms quickly in small children but also fades more rapidly. One speculation is that an explicit memory could disappear, but the fear memory could stay. In this way, a person could fear heights without remembering an early-childhood tumble from a high place.

Despite having multiple memory systems, the brain can deceive us with fading memories, drift in memory (where people may remember the same event differently), and simply inaccurate recollections.

For example, source amnesia occurs when context is separated from facts; you recall a fact but not how you learned that fact. It's common for people to remember a falsehood long after they have forgotten the accompanying disclaimer; repetition of a falsehood can also become a memory of the falsehood as fact. Repetition strengthens a memory as it is recalled and reprocessed, turning it into a general fact. ■

Important Terms

amygdala: An almond-shaped nucleus beneath the rostral pole of the temporal lobe; involved in the processing of emotions, particularly fear.

post-traumatic stress disorder (PTSD): A disorder characterized by anxiety and fear acquired because of a traumatic event.

1. The phenomenon of memory rewriting can help account for why two persons recall the same event very differently. Identify such an episode that you have experienced with a friend or a loved one.

2. Practice using the "consider the opposite" strategy the next time you encounter a piece of information that you would be normally inclined to accept (or reject) based on your beliefs.

Learning, Studying, and Sleep
Lecture 14

Learning involves changes in the brain. Learning is likely to arise from cellular rules, ... the idea that cells that fire together wire together, and the converse: out of sync, lose your link. So in general, neuronal change is a phenomenon that may underlie learning. ... One form of learning [is] synaptic plasticity, ... a form of change in which the connections between neurons change in their strength.

Just as the brain has evolved to help us survive, so have our ideas of how the brain works changed over the millennia. A common idea was that the brain changed rapidly during our first five years of life, then became a fixed object. But the brain generates behavior, which changes as it responds to environmental events and experience, so something in the brain must change to allow us to learn. What do we know about how the brain changes and learns?

In 350 B.C.E., Aristotle lacked sophisticated knowledge of biology but posited an important idea: As we recall experience, we are taking advantage of some natural sequence of events that happens in our heads: the fact that one thought has, by nature, another that succeeds it in a regular order. In 1908, William James proposed the law of neural habit, or the idea that a pattern of brain activity that leads to another can recur, like wearing a rut in your brain. In 1949, the founder of cognitive neuroscience, Donald Hebb, proposed cell assembly as a mechanism for memory storage; this is the idea that neurons that have fired together because of an experience are more

Sleep has restorative value.

43

likely to activate together during recall of that same experience. In other words, cells that fire together wire together.

A cornerstone of modern ideas on learning is **synaptic plasticity**, the idea that neuronal change may underlie learning. Researchers study how the neuron could change to become more sensitive to firing. Changes could occur at the synapses, the major place where learning occurs. The following possibilities occur on the same time scale as short-term memory: (1) increase in receptors, (2) presynaptic terminal more likely to release a transmitter (increased excitability), (3) possible changes in connection strength, and (4) formation of new synapses.

Short-term and long-term memory are different animals with different properties. Long-term memory separates facts from their context and stores them in a more general way. The transfer of short-term to long-term out of the medial temporal lobe system into the neocortex is called consolidation, an aspect of learning.

Consolidation requires time between learning sessions. Information that seems to be permanently stored in fact undergoes constant change as memories are reprocessed and consolidated. Memory is far more fluid than commonly thought. That's why two 4-hour study sessions are more productive than one 8-hour session (the power of spaced study). Consolidation also requires sleep.

We once thought sleep shut down much of the brain, but it's more a change in the overall pattern of brain activity. Sleep seems to have restorative or repairing value. A lack of sleep disrupts or derails consolidation of memory; perhaps the memories of the day's events are replayed and consolidated during sleep. The brain could use this time to separate general information from the original context, strengthening memories by replaying and reprocessing them.

The phenomenon of priming is one form of learning in which we're exposed to information without forming an explicit representation of it; we don't remember the information but can, in fact, use it for something else. For example, students given a test question about material they haven't covered are "primed" or subconsciously directed to pay attention to specific information in upcoming classes. ∎

synaptic plasticity: The dynamic property of synapses; believed to underlie learning and memory.

Questions to Consider

1. Name two study strategies that are suggested by the principles described in this lecture and the previous one.

2. Explain Donald Hebb's speculation on how an experience might be translated into long-term change in the brain.

Willpower and Mental Work
Lecture 15

> Willpower can be exercised ... like a muscle, and you can wear it out. ... Like a muscle, willpower seems to become stronger with use. ... Short-term use of willpower depletes the existing willpower supply, but long-term exercise of willpower actually increases the size of the willpower pool, metaphorically speaking. ...The willpower muscle, whatever it is, gets tired from exercise short term but can be built up long term.

If you despair that you lack enough willpower to stick to your diet and drop five pounds, keep in mind that neocortical plasticity is your friend. That's because the ability of our brain to change means that we can exercise our willpower like a muscle, making it stronger to effect desired behaviors.

Willpower (self-control) for many tasks draws on a single, shared, finite mental resource that can be measured in a lab. Young children can be tested for willpower. For example, in a famous experiment at Stanford University, four-year-olds who were able to defer reward in order to double it (refraining from eating a marshmallow for 15 minutes to earn a second one) grew up to be teens who scored better on SAT exams and fared better academically overall than the four-year-olds who couldn't resist eating the treat almost immediately. They were also judged to be more dependable and better adjusted. Self-control is a better predictor of later success than IQ.

This deferral of reward is an example of executive function, involving the **prefrontal cortex**. Other brain structures involved in self-restraint are the **frontal cortex** and the anterior cingulated cortex.

Trying to do multiple tasks can wear out our willpower, but what exactly is it that wears out? We don't really know, but evidence points in a couple of directions. The prefrontal cortex uses lots of sugar, which means that depleted blood sugar might be the limiting resource when we exercise willpower. You can see this by drinking a glass of lemonade (with sugar, not artificial sweetener) after completing a task; the blood sugar rises, and you regain concentration to complete the next task. Another possibility is that some neurotransmitter or some substrate, some chemical that's needed to manufacture a neurotransmitter, runs out.

Increasing willpower involves the neocortex, which seems like a very plausible place for changes to occur in the brain whenever experiences are stored. We've spoken in past lectures of the brain's plasticity, its ability to change on the neuronal level. This leads to the question: If willpower requires neocortical structures, is it plastic, too? Happily, the answer is yes. Willpower training involves some kind of activity to focus on, some mediating object that helps people stay focused and maintain attention. For example, using your non-dominant hand for two weeks to brush your teeth can lead to increased willpower. People who tried this reported other benefits, such as reducing their impulsive spending and decreasing alcohol use and smoking, among other benefits. Some activities seem to draw on the same mental resource. Other willpower training can include urban citizenship programs, learning to play an instrument or sport, and military training.

> **Willpower training involves some kind of activity to focus on, some mediating object that helps people stay focused and maintain attention.**

How does your brain increase willpower? Neural activity in the form of exercising your self-control may drive rearrangement of circuitry in the neocortex; this plasticity is a possible explanation for what may underlie the buildup of willpower. ∎

Important Terms

frontal cortex: A recently evolved region of the brain that plays a central role in executive cognitive function, decision making, gratification postponement, and regulation of the limbic system.

prefrontal cortex: Part of the frontal lobe implicated in working memory.

1. Describe evidence for the idea that willpower is a finite mental resource, drawn upon for a wide variety of life activities.

2. Describe evidence for the idea that willpower seems to have the capacity to be built up like a muscle.

Lecture 15: Willpower and Mental Work

Work, Play, and Stress
Lecture 16

When your house is on fire, it's not time to paint the kitchen. Just as it's not time to paint the kitchen, if you're in some kind of emergency situation, your brain and body need all the energy they can get their mitts on in order to get you away from the danger.

W orking against an inexorably approaching deadline is one example of a stressor, something that upsets our equilibrium, or set point, and makes our brain initiate what all vertebrates experience: a stress response. This set point can depend on circumstances; if there's one set point, we refer to **homeostasis**, the normal way in which the nervous systems regulate our organs. If the set point is variable, such as blood pressure adapting to whether you're sitting or standing, it's called allostasis. Stress response seeks to restore homeostasis.

The stress response is mediated by **hormones** called **glucocorticoids**, which act on a time scale of minutes to hours. But whether the stressor is swerving to avoid hitting another vehicle or waiting to go on stage to accept an award, the body has a surprisingly similar set of responses to help us adapt. These can be quick, signaled by epinephrine (adrenaline) through the **autonomic nervous system,** or slower, signaled through the stress hormone cortisol. Epinephrine is released throughout the body; norepinephrine, in the brain; and cortisol goes both to the body and to the brain. Our senses are sharpened; our pulse and breathing quicken; and in high-stress situations, our brain shuts down nonessential systems and can even dull our sense of pain. Even anticipating or witnessing a stressful situation can elevate stress hormones.

Besides these short-term stress responses, persistent stress can cause long-term damage to the body and to the brain. It weakens the immune system, causes ulcers, atrophies the hippocampus (responsible for navigation, memory, and learning), and interrupts formation of neurons, among other negative outcomes.

Where do stress responses begin and where in the nervous system do they go? A common origin for stress response is the amygdala, necessary for emotional response and interpreting emotional events. The amygdala triggers multiple responses, including the stress response, avoidance behavior, and increased vigilance.

The hypothalamic pituitary adrenal (HPA) axis is a set of organs essential for the stress response. When the amygdala responds to a stressor, it activates the **hypothalamus**, which regulates body temperature, appetite, and sexual behavior. In this situation, the hypothalamus secretes a substance that, in turn, triggers the pituitary gland, which activates the **adrenal gland**. This gland secretes cortisol and epinephrine, also called adrenaline, which helps the amygdala consolidate memory and is responsible for what premed students call fight, flight, fright, and sex. The fight-or-flight response is activated in a short time scale; then cortisol acts on a longer time scale to shut down nonessential functions to conserve resources and allow response.

Walter Cannon, discoverer of the fight-or-flight response.

National Library of Medicine.

Play is one way to fight the ill effects of stress. It is one modern activity that triggers allostatic responses in the short term without leading to long-term problems. Play is a focused activity but more varied: During a game, you do one thing, then another thing. Typically, play does not trigger a long-term stress response. Play does trigger some short-term emotional responses: We secrete epinephrine often when we play because our blood pressure goes up. But play does not lead to chronic damage. Play can simulate real-world situations without creating long-term burdens on the brain; thus, play is a relatively healthy counterpart to work. ■

Important Terms

adrenal glands: Glands located above the kidneys; under stress, they release catecholamines and cortisol.

autonomic nervous system (ANS): A series of neural pathways originating in the hypothalamus, hindbrain, and brainstem and projecting throughout the body; it regulates all sorts of nonconscious, automatic physiological changes throughout the body.

glucocorticoids: A class of steroid hormones secreted during stress. They include cortisol (a.k.a. hydrocortisone) and synthetic versions, such as prednisone and dexamethasone.

homeostasis: "Balance"; as used here, for example, balance between sympathetic and parasympathetic portions of the autonomic nervous system.

hormones: Blood-borne chemical messengers between cells.

hypothalamus: A limbic structure that receives heavy inputs from other parts of the limbic system; plays a central role in regulating both the autonomic nervous system and hormone release.

Questions to Consider

1. What are the positive benefits of the brain's stress response?

2. Describe the major roles of epinephrine and cortisol in the stress response and the clinical syndromes that result when they are not present.

Biological Timekeepers and Jet Lag
Lecture 17

> Similarly, there are people who cannot entrain their rhythm very well, or they have strange day/night habits. So these people are like mutant [golden] hamsters; they seem to be up at all hours. ... Perhaps there are maybe these inborn mechanisms that people have that make them have odd day/night cycling.

Got rhythm? Even if you can't keep time with the song on the radio, your body has an exquisite master clock that drives the brain and the body's natural rhythms, in particular, the circadian rhythm. From the Latin *circa dias* ("about a day"), the circadian rhythm is a form of allostasis, the keeping of our body systems on an even keel. It helps the brain and body be ready for different events that are likely to happen at different parts of the day and regulates sleep, body temperature, appetite, and other functions.

The circadian rhythm is a cycle synchronized with the daily cycle of sunrise and sunset. Even so, it isn't just a response to the immediate presence of light. People kept in a room with no lighting cues maintain their 22- to 24-hour circadian rhythm at first, then start to drift across the clock, gradually starting to wake a little later and becoming out of synch with the rest of the world. Plants also evidence some kind of internal biological clock, some mechanism of cycling of about 24 hours. Similar networks of communication are present in a large number of animals and other types of organisms.

Genes that control the circadian rhythm form part

© iStockphoto/Thinkstock.

Some golden hamsters have a mutation that alters their circadian rhythm.

of a network of proteins that interact with one another to maintain a rhythm that goes for about 24 hours, then restarts, sustaining the rhythm even in the absence of light. Still, the biggest factor influencing the circadian rhythm is light itself. Our eyes have retinal ganglion cells dedicated to detecting light for entraining the circadian rhythm.

The hypothalamus is packed with different regions that are important for regulating various functions; one of those regions important for the circadian rhythm is called the suprachiasmatic nucleus, the master clock. It receives signals from the eye and generates its own signal, controlling the other clocks, or networks, throughout the body. Animals with damage to the suprachiasmatic nucleus will wake and sleep at odd hours.

Light from the **retina** also triggers the pineal gland to make the hormone melatonin. Melatonin levels rise in the evening, peak around the onset of sleep, and go down again in the early morning before you awake.

Traveling quickly across multiple time zones can cause jet lag (when your circadian rhythm is set to a different time from the external day/night cycle in the world), which is the result of our brains having these clocks that keep running independently. Jet lag makes it difficult to get to sleep and causes drowsiness, lack of alertness, and even digestive problems. Persistent disruption of the circadian rhythm has ill health effects: Persistent jet lag over a long time can reduce the volume in the temporal lobe (involved in memory and learning) and result in poor memory. The associated stress hormones can also damage the brain. People who do shift work for years have related problems. A commonly used remedy for dealing with jet lag is a dose of melatonin at night to encourage sleep. Exercise triggers secretion of melatonin, but the biggest influence in resetting the clock is light. ■

Important Term

retina (neural retina): Multilayered sheet of neurons located at the back of the eyeball, and derived from the diencephalon in development.

1. When traveling over multiple time zones, do you find it harder to adjust going east or going west? Do you consider yourself a morning person or an evening person? Given the properties of the circadian rhythm, how might these answers be related?

2. Which brain region is the master clock in determining the circadian rhythm? What body regions are known to follow the lead of the master clock?

The Hidden Talents of Infants
Lecture 18

From infancy, people have talents that are fundamental to how the brain works. These talents guide us and are used from ... birth all the way to adulthood. This picture does not leave much room for the tabula rasa concept, the idea that babies are born with the potential to develop in any direction. Instead, ... the cognitive talents that babies have in early life, their abilities to notice and to learn and to think, are essential for directing the development of their brains.

B rain development reflects our theme of change that runs through this course. Our brain constantly undergoes changes, thanks to inborn mechanisms, natural processes as we age, and influences from the environment and our experiences. At no time does the brain change more rapidly than it does before birth and in the first six years after birth. In this lecture, we'll focus on infant capabilities.

Evidence has debunked the Mozart myth, the idea that playing classical music to fetuses or babies can make them smarter just from passive listening; evidence has also debunked the claim that children can learn to read at age 1. Infants haven't learned the basics of hearing languages or simple tones. Moreover, scientists have also debunked the tabula rasa concept, the idea that babies are blanks that will indiscriminately learn anything that is thrown at them. Instead, they go through stages, in which they are able to absorb specific types of information rapidly.

The human brain is among the largest among mammals, with a large neocortex that occupies three-quarters of total brain volume. This brain size means that most development must occur after birth, making us altricial; in other words, we are born dependent and with special needs for biological support. During the rapid brain development that takes place before age 6, we acquire language, social skills, and other knowledge that eclipses our learning during the rest of our lives.

Childhood is marked by sensitive periods, when specific types of information are easiest to learn. For example, languages learned by age 6 will be spoken without an accent. Primary and multiple languages are represented in overlapping parts of the brain.

Babies' slow motor development used to be taken to mean that they were also mentally slow, but their minds are actually complex even at birth, something we can test experimentally. For instance, babies notice novelty; a newborn sucks faster when seeing something new. They also understand object permanence and have a sense of number.

Beginning at age 3 months, babies exhibit five general capacities:

- Can detect the probability of events, a key component of learning.

- Use coincidences to draw conclusions about cause and effect.

- Can distinguish objects (solid, no independent movement) from agents (something implying social and mental intention, capable of independent movement).

- Can organize information into categories and people into groups. This trait enables a baby to think sensibly about newly encountered objects, but it is also the root of later stereotyping and prejudice.

- Can select relevant information for attention and discard irrelevant information. Babies are less selective in this than adults but still show innate biases, particularly for faces and moving objects. Attention is a crucial skill and increases the brain's ability to learn.

Babies are biologically pre-prepared, ready to learn specific things. That's why they acquire human speech instead of imitating the dishwasher or the family cat. ∎

1. Name three innate capacities that 3-month-old infants have for learning from their environment.

2. What key experimental technique allows psychologists to test sensory and perceptual capabilities of infants?

The Mozart Myth and Active Learning
Lecture 19

> Think of it as like this: When you're building a house, you can decide where you want to arrange the bedrooms. You can decide exactly where you want the windows and so on. But once the house has been built, changes are harder. You can rearrange the furniture or replace the furniture, but the floor plan is set.

Many parents fret over whether their young children can learn to excel without a roster of extracurricular activities, but it's important to realize that many aspects of brain development are preprogrammed and don't require anything beyond normal experiences. Further, most environments are sufficient for normal development. The key principles of early mental development don't include extraordinary learning activities, just active engagement and age-appropriate experiences.

In utero, the brain requires no experiences at all, because it's busy growing large numbers of nonselective neurons, forming axons, and migrating neurons to final destinations. After this process of explosive growth, the brain begins to edit itself. In the first two years of life, neurons that aren't used die and are removed, a regressive process.

There is some evidence that, during those important first years, intellectual ability may be enhanced by exposure to intellectually stimulating activities. For example, the IQ scores of children up to age 3 correlate with the number of words they hear each day, with higher scores related to the greater number of words heard. When these children are tested again in third grade, the correlation remains. In another example of active engagement, children who learn to play a musical instrument have better spatial reasoning skills than those who don't take music lessons. The engagement and practice of a skill is more likely to trigger active neuronal firing, leading to better development. Parents should encourage children to be active producers, not passive consumers.

The Flynn effect describes the steady increase in IQ scores in children in industrialized countries since World War II, pointing to the idea that better nutrition and a more complex, stimulating environment (including more social interaction, thanks to improved mass communication) may enhance brain development. This trend has leveled off in recent years.

Active engagement is effective in teaching certain skills or concepts only when the brain is ready to learn that specific skill or concept. Some forms of brain plasticity are no longer available after a certain age. For example, a scientist

Children today have a more intellectually stimulating environment than those of 100 years ago.

blinded in childhood but restored to sight through surgery in adulthood had trouble distinguishing shadows from objects; he finally got a seeing-eye dog. He missed some critical context early in life, when the brain was ready to learn what a shadow was versus an object.

Another age-appropriate experience is acquiring language, best done before age 6. Early learners of multiple languages learn to speak as natives with no accent. The Broca's area of the brain (the brain region that produces speech) in multilingual children lights up no matter which language is spoken; for adult learners, other areas light up for the later-acquired language. The window for learning accent closes sooner than for learning grammar, both for spoken languages and for signed languages: Hand movements that are not entirely natural seem to correspond to the sign language equivalent of having an accent. ■

1. What are the roles of passive and active experience in shaping brain development?

2. What does the per-generation rate of the Flynn effect tell you about the role of genes and environment in brain development? How might this limit what we can say about the innate abilities of a particular group, such as a race?

Childhood and Adolescence
Lecture 20

Myelination is not complete until people reach their early 20s. Again, that suggests a possible physical basis for changes in self-control and changes in the ability to pay attention. So there is this sense that one gets from these changes in brain structure that there is a physical basis in the kinds of capacities that change as we go through adolescence and reach early adulthood.

A 6-year-old's brain already has experienced its most rapid growth and has almost all of the neurons it will have, but even in adolescence, some brain systems are still developing. During childhood, the brain grows larger but doesn't add neurons. Instead, it adds complexity to neurons and changes mental capacities that correlate with developing brain regions, such as increasing self-control.

Scans of children and adolescents show how the brain develops from the back to the front. Regions necessary for sensation, movement, and many basic emotional and sexual responses are fully formed first. Frontal regions necessary for self-restraint, short-term memory, and future planning are not necessarily fully mature in young adults. This physically changing brain results in changing behaviors. Risk-seeking decreases and hazardous behavior declines after the teen years. Children diagnosed with attention deficit disorder often grow out of it as their brains mature.

As growing neocortical neurons send out dendrites, they increase the thickness of the **gray matter**. Although the eventual thickness of the gray matter is similar, the timing of this change is important. Thickening happens later in high-achieving children, suggesting that appropriately timed growth is an important element. In addition to this gain in bulk, a final stage in brain maturation includes adding a sheath of protein and fat to the axons. This protein is called myelin, and it allows the fast coordination of action, helping impulses travel faster. Because the brain develops from the back of the skull to the front, myelination comes last to the prefrontal regions that control executive function, which entails self-control and planning. This process is not complete until people reach their early 20s.

Mental capacities develop on their own and in response to external events. These capacities have a range of trainability, highlighted below:

- IQ is an innate quality that is difficult to train, although problem-solving intelligence can be improved by working on memory.

- Temperament has genetic and environmental components. Surprisingly, peers have more influence on a child's temperament than parents do, although careful nurturing by parents can help to improve a difficult temperament.

- Will power (self-regulation) probably involves plasticity in the neocortex, the brain systems related to executive function. This trait is an early indicator of academic success in later years and can be trained. Self-control can be taught as early as age 3 by elaborate, imaginative play, including intricate games. Some schools use a program called Tools of the Mind to teach preschoolers self-control and restraint.

- Multitasking is a myth because what we really are doing is switching from one cognitively demanding task to another. That switching between tasks causes a delay. Training can minimize this delay, however. Evidence shows that playing complex video games may involve some element of training for multitasking, because such games require planning and switching tasks, two skills that can broaden the bottleneck in brain processing. ■

Important Term

gray matter: Areas where there are collections of neuronal cell bodies.

1. How might complex play cause long-term changes in brain circuits?

2. In the development of a child's temperament, parental influences may matter less than the daily peer and school environment. Why might this be?

Handedness—Sports, Speech, and Presidents
Lecture 21

The general theme is that left-handers are more variable than right-handers. They are more likely to get a high SAT score. They are more likely to be more creative. But they are also more likely to be criminals or mentally retarded. So there is this greater variation in left-handedness.

W hy is an important assistant called a right-hand man and not a left-hand man? Why do we favor one hand over another, beginning in infancy? Of all the animals, only humans predominantly favor right-handedness. Other species have either no preference or favor one hand for one skill and the other hand for another skill. Only 1 in 10 people favor left-handedness, an attribute with negative cultural myths but one that fascinates neuroscientists, who believe that it arises from a mix of genetic and environmental causes.

Myths about left-handedness include beliefs that left-handers have shorter life spans and are more accident-prone and the idea that right-handedness is just better than left-handedness; these ideas have been debunked. There are no known biological disadvantages for left-handedness.

What is true is that left-handers are more variable than right-handers both in the high and low end of achievement, and they seem to think differently in many ways, ranging from creative arts to SAT scores. There are more lefties in the creative arts (Pablo Picasso was one), and lefties have unusual math skills; dealing with a right-handed world encourages divergent thinking—finding counterintuitive solutions to problems. Interactive sports (baseball, fencing, tennis, and boxing) are dominated by lefties, which may be because left-handers' better-developed right hemispheres give them an advantage. Another explanation is that both right-handed and left-handed athletes have less experience facing a left-handed opponent. Both right-handers and left-handers have more difficulty anticipating a lefty's next move. Lefties are also more likely to be criminals or mentally retarded.

Interactive sports are dominated by left-handed people.

Neuroscientists have multiple theories on how handedness is determined, including genetic, experience-dependent, and environmental/early developmental models. Early life preference can lead to a cascading effect in which practice leads to eventual dominance of one hand. A brain injury to the brain's left hemisphere, which controls the body's right side, could require a person to compensate and use the left hand. This could account for left-handers' unusually high rate of neurological disorders. Or perhaps a person began with an innate preference but made an early decision to use the left hand.

Six of the past 12 U.S. presidents have been left-handers and noted orators, illustrating the belief that there is some fundamental link between hand dominance and language, which is lateralized, or processed, in both hemispheres. The left side (Broca's and Wernicke's areas) processes inputs and outputs. The right side processes nonverbal, non-language abilities, including prosody, or the melody of speech, its emotional content. Most people process language on the left side of the brain, but a study showed that 10% of left-handers processed language on the right side of the brain; another 15% processed language on both sides—something rare in right-handers. Why is this? Perhaps using the left hand early in life allows both sides of the brain to process language. Maybe verbal and manual dexterity go together because they use common neural structures. ∎

Questions to Consider

1. Do left-handers have shorter life pans than right-handers? What is the problem with the evidence?

2. What is the connection between handedness and language? What evidence does brain imaging provide on this subject?

Reaching the Top of the Mountain—Aging
Lecture 22

So what we have here is evidence that in the most fundamental sense, the adult brain can change throughout life by making new neurons. This process of neurogenesis is variable—it can be regulated by experience—and so, in fact, it can be different from person to person, different from animal to animal, depending on circumstances.

W hether we're able to do it gracefully or not, aging is a process that sees some of our functions decline—beginning as early as our 30s—but sees other capacities remain and even improve. This process reflects the principle that the brain changes throughout life, even making neurons long past the time when such development was commonly thought possible.

In normal aging, we see structural changes in the brain, as well as behavioral changes in everyday life. Aging brings shrinkage in brain volume and changes in synaptic strength, both with the birth of a few neurons and the loss of others, and changes in

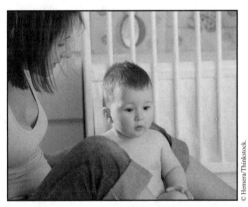

Parenting can encourage neuron generation.

dendritic branching and synapses, where the brain actions are carried out. Loss of branching is part of what's responsible for decline in functions, such as memory. Loss of branching may be reversible, but it's harder to replace lost neurons.

The capacity for memory peaks in our 30s, then begins to decline; other functions that decline later in aging are spatial navigation, a capacity shared with some forms of memory, and executive function. This last function includes working memory (what was my friend's phone number again?), speed of response, pattern comparison, processing speed, and self-control. These capacities begin to decline in our 70s and 80s.

It's not all bad news, however. Adult neurogenesis, discovered in 1962 by Joseph Altman, means that the brain (specifically, the hippocampus and olfactory bulb) continues to make a few neurons as we age. And the brain's structural plasticity—its ability to change its structure on the cellular level in response to external events—means that we can have some influence on its natural decline. Stress and **depression** hasten the death of neurons, but active parenting (for both mothers and fathers) and exercise can encourage neuron generation and synaptic strength.

Some functions remain largely unchanged as we age, while others even improve. We generally retain well-learned skills, such as the ability to ride a bike, professional skills, and vocabulary and factual knowledge. (The information is still there, but anomic aphasia, or the Library of Congress effect, will make us slower in recalling it.) Our emotional control improves with age. Our emotional responses become better modulated, and the overall balance tilts toward positive emotion in our 70s and 80s. Neuroscientists suggest two reasons for this functional retention: We have a way to build multiple strategies for solving problems, and we have a cognitive reserve capacity to compensate for neuronal loss.

Unnatural changes that can afflict us as we age include **dementia**, such as Alzheimer's disease; **stroke**; and Parkinson's, which we discussed in an earlier lecture. Alzheimer's is a growing problem as life spans increase, with its likelihood statistically doubling every five years after age 55. Strokes, depriving the brain of oxygen and glucose, are caused by clots or a burst blood vessel. If treated with a specific drug within the first three hours, damage from a clot-induced stroke can be repaired. ■

dementia: A progressive mental deterioration.

depression: A disorder of "mood" characterized by an internal subjective state of hopelessness and despair.

stroke: Any acute neurological event related to impairment in blood flow or circulation in the central nervous system; can be hemorrhagic or ischemic.

Questions to Consider

1. What capacities decline with age? What capacities stay the same or improve?

2. You think that someone may be having a stroke. How much time do you have to get to a hospital for rapid treatment? Where is the nearest hospital to you that has the appropriate resources?

"Brain Exercise" and Real Exercise
Lecture 23

This activity that leads to larger changes is physical exercise, in other words, real exercise. ... Cicero, around 65 B.C., said, "It is exercise alone that supports the spirits and keeps the mind in vigor." ... [In contrast, it was] Mark Twain who said, "I take my only exercise acting as pallbearer at the funerals of my friends who exercise regularly." Clearly opinion is mixed from old times.

The aphorisms "use it or lose it," "sound mind and sound body," and "what's good for the heart is good for the brain" embody scientific findings that exercise, both mental and physical, really does help us retain cognitive functions as we age. We don't completely understand how this is so, but it's encouraging to know that we can take an active role in maintaining brain health for as long as possible.

Brain training, or mental exercise, is a hot topic and big business. By 2007, the brain training market was $80 million and growing. Puzzles, pattern recognition exercises, Sudoku and the like, along with working memory tasks, are purported to improve memory and other cognitive tasks—a claim neither strongly supported nor strongly refuted by scientific evidence. Practicing a brain exercise may improve your functioning in that particular task for a short while, but the benefit doesn't extend to other cognitive abilities. Improving your ability to remember a list of words, for example, does not improve spatial reasoning.

Some brain training is effective: It is often possible to get a more significant change in reaction time through brain training. One possibility is that reaction time is something that changes through natural biological mechanisms; it can also be trained through such exercises as playing video games.

Education helps retain cognitive abilities, possibly because it provides mental tools for engagement, helping us appreciate complexity in the world, enjoy art, or solve problems. Education gives us tools for thinking. An intellectually engaged lifestyle correlates with retained function in later life. Brain health benefits if you have multiple and complex hobbies (such as playing bridge), if you travel, learn a new language late in life, or learn musical instrument. An intellectually engaged lifestyle could help with our cognitive reserves, rather like gathering nuts for the winter.

Even more effective than brain-training exercises is physical exercise, particularly regular exercise maintained over a long period. Aerobic exercise is especially protective of brain functions. Exercise can ease depression, improve executive function (memory and planning), and dramatically reduce the risk of dementia—even when an exercise program isn't begun until middle age or much later. People with a sedentary lifestyle who adopt a regular exercise regimen in their 60s cut their risk of developing Alzheimer's by half.

> **Even more effective than brain-training exercises is physical exercise, particularly regular exercise maintained over a long period.**

Exercise does many things that could improve our cognitive abilities. It increases blood flow to the brain; triggers secretion of neurotrophic and atrophic factors, which improve dendritic growth; secretes naturally occurring opiates (endorphins); reduces stress hormone secretion; and improves cardiovascular health, which in turn reduces risk of stroke. The benefits of physical exercise last only up to a few weeks after the exercise ceases, however. You have to keep doing it, but you will see a large benefit. Other interventions that are good for the heart are also good for brain health. These include drinking red wine (in moderation), taking prescribed anti-clotting drugs, and eating brightly colored foods rich with antioxidants. ■

Questions to Consider

1. What is the relative size of the benefit from brain training software compared with physical exercise? If you had $200 to spend on training software or on athletic gear/club membership, which would you choose?

Animal and Human Personality
Lecture 24

It is possible to take personality tests of these same types that are applied to animals and give them to people, as well. In fact, of course, they are more prevalent in human psychology because it turns out that there is much more of an interest in human personality than there is in octopus personality.

The brain factor that differentiates us from one another is personality, a strongly inheritable property that is determined by hundreds of gene combinations and by environmental influences—but hardly at all, it turns out, by parents.

Personality, or temperament, is a difficult thing to study because it's not quantifiable; that is, it can't be measured or scored. Still, we have a powerful tendency to impute motivation to other people and even to other things. Scientists have studied animal behavior and catalogued individual traits in an attempt to understand the biological reasons for them. These ethologists discovered that certain traits tend to go together in clusters. For example, the cluster traits for extroversion include sociability, outgoingness, and assertiveness. Two important personality tests are used to assess specific traits. The five-factor model (FFM) assesses openness to experience, conscientiousness, extroversion, agreeableness, and neuroticism, all of which show strong inheritability. The Meyers-Briggs test classifies traits into four categories.

What is the reason for so much variation in personality? Individual traits can be an advantage or a disadvantage depending on environmental conditions. Great variation gives the population in general a greater chance of survival no matter the environmental conditions. For example, a daring animal would get more food and be more successful with a low density of predators, but that same daring trait would increase the animal's chance of falling prey if there was a higher density of predators. In that situation, the more timid animals that are content to eat scraps and avoid predators would have a better survival rate.

There seems to be a 30% to 50% inheritable component to personality and a 50% to 70% environmental component. We don't know what causes environment-induced personality development, and we haven't identified specific genes that cause specific personality traits. Instead, clusters of genes, perhaps hundreds of clusters, make up an individual trait, making them polygenic.

Anxiety is associated with shortage of a specific protein responsible for the uptake of serotonin, a neuromodulator involved in mood.

Half the variation of anxiety is inherited. Anxiety is associated with shortage of a specific protein responsible for the uptake of serotonin, a neuromodulator involved in mood. But this protein plays a small role. Novelty-seeking involves dopamine receptors. Dopamine and serotonin activity seem to have some role in predicting personality, but the contribution they make so far seems to be small. These findings point to the possibility of understanding how personality is determined by genes and by the environment. The mechanisms of personality are still a mystery, and the focus is on neurotransmitters. This topic is only just beginning to unfold.

Personality starts to manifest itself when a baby is about 3 months old; from there, a combination of innate mechanisms and individual experience influences the eventual outcome of personality development. Parents really have little influence over their children's personalities, except when a child is shy or anxious. Shy babies may be shy toddlers and children, but this tendency usually diminishes. A very small minority persist in this behavior into adulthood, where they have a high risk of anxiety disorders. However, parents who are calm and nurturing can help teach the shy or anxious child important coping skills to overcome these difficulties and become successful adults.

Personality changes as we grow, staying malleable until about the age of 30, when it becomes more stable. It is most stable between the ages of 50 to 70. ∎

1. How much can parents influence a child's personality development after he or she is born?

2. In what cases can a parent have an important positive influence on a child's temperament?

Intelligence, Genes, and Environment
Lecture 25

> This excess brain, EQ, the amount of the brain occupied by forebrain, varies among species. It turns out that those variable proportions in particular are very predictive of problem solving and tool making.

This lecture discusses the genetics of intelligence and its environmental influences in terms of some controversial questions: Is it possible to increase the average intelligence of the population? Are there measurable differences between the sexes? Are there measurable differences between races? Can a finding be statistically significant yet have a small effect? What do averages and statistically significant differences tell us about individuals?

Quite early on, researchers observed that there is no correlation between brain size and intellectual accomplishments. Size difference has no direct correlation with performance. But interest in correlating brain size and biological factors with intelligence has been around for a long time—in particular, in the eugenics movement that took place between about 1900 and 1940. The hope of the eugenics proponents was to identify differences among groups and, perhaps, find ways to make the human race better. But group differences that are strong in one generation don't necessarily carry over into the next; thus, there is difficulty with the idea that a difference can be bred in the population.

Intelligence has multiple aspects, one of which is "fluid intelligence": the ability to reason through a problem you've never seen before. Fluid intelligence is correlated with working memory, which is the ability to hold information in your brain for several seconds, and with the ability to resist distractions. These capacities require the action of specific brain regions, some of which are in the **basal ganglia**. One is the striatum, a brain region that releases dopamine into parts of the frontal cortex; dopamine is both a reward signal and important in attention, in particular, for initiating and directing actions and thoughts and in updating information and working memory. Other regions important for fluid intelligence seem to be those with which the striatum communicates, particularly the prefrontal cortex, structures that seem important for resisting distraction.

The role of genetics in determining intelligence is complex and less well developed than the study of personality, but comparisons of identical twins with fraternal twins suggest that the prenatal environment appears to contribute about 20% of the variation in fluid intelligence. A key caveat here is that studies that show heritability of intelligence have been done in middle-class households with normal resources, without deprivation. This fact is critical because deprivation, as an environmental factor, is important in determining fluid intelligence. When the environment is bad, the influence of genes drops to as low as 10%. In general, the evidence points toward the conclusion that intelligence is predicted by both genetic and environmental factors. Under conditions of deprivation, environment wins. Under conditions of plenty, genes and environment seem to make approximately equal contributions.

But are fluid intelligence and problem solving really the right way to define intelligence? Objections to this definition include the idea that our brains have multiple capacities, such as emotional intelligence, the ability to read people's emotions and respond appropriately. Another objection is that test performance can be influenced by expectations, both external and internal. A third objection is a basic one: Tests only measure test-taking ability. All the consequences that come later in life, success and all the things we all know from everyday experience, don't necessarily correlate with fluid intelligence or any other kind of intelligence. ■

Important Term

basal ganglia: A number of nuclei located subcortically in the forebrain. Many of the basal ganglia nuclei are involved in the extrapyramidal motor system.

1. Some people argue for the role of family life and genetics in determining intelligence, while others argue for the importance of resources, such as school funding. Considering the heritability of intelligence in normal and deprived environments, who is right? Are both right?

2. Describe a good pre-test strategy for maximizing performance on an exam.

The Weather in Your Brain—Emotions
Lecture 26

Emotions are organized brain responses to events in the world around us. So basically, emotions are ways to organize or ways of dealing with information.

In some sense, we can think of emotions as a means our brains use to contain knowledge, accumulate it over evolutionary time, and organize it as strategies and responses to be passed on across generations. Emotions are organized brain responses to events in the world around us. They help us focus on critical information and motivate us to shape our behavior, get what we want and avoid what we fear, and move to a previous or desired state. Emotions also are critical in influencing decision-making.

Following Darwin's observations of animals, theories of emotion were propounded by William James, who said that we meet only a small fraction of our brain's potential, and Walter Cannon, a pioneer in understanding the fight-or-flight response.

William James and a Danish scientist named Carl Lange proposed a theory of emotion called the James-Lange theory, which suggested that we experience emotion in response to physiological changes and that those changes then change our perception of what we are feeling. James and Lange believed that those physiological changes were the emotion and that emotion consisted of a feedback loop in which the brain told the body what to do and the body told the brain what was going on.

However, Walter Cannon, the discoverer of "fight or flight," and another scientist named Philip Bard pointed out that in fact, there's a problem with the James-Lange theory: That is, emotional experience can occur independently of emotional expression. Furthermore, some physical reactions are associated with multiple emotional states. For example, both fear and anger are associated with an increased heart rate, inhibition of digestion, and increased sweating. A physical condition, such as a fever, can also lead to these reactions. Thus, it seems that fear cannot be purely a consequence of physiological changes. There must be something more to the story.

Different responses can share common neurotransmitters. Consider, for example, the adrenaline response. Adrenaline responses can be associated with different kinds of emotions, and to some extent, we can harness these emotions. For instance, if you get on a roller coaster, you get an adrenaline rush. Maybe you're afraid of it, or maybe you enjoy it. That same adrenaline rush can make the experience enjoyable or horrible.

The study of brain regions that are involved in emotional response goes back about 100 years. Broca noticed that there was a ring of structures around the **brain stem** that seemed different from the rest of the brain because of either their connections or their appearance. He called this area the "limbic lobe," "limbic" meaning peripheral region, or ring-like region. Papez, a later neurologist, suggested that there was an emotion system, a circuit of brain regions, many of which were collected near the midline in the brain, now called the **limbic system.** ■

Important Terms

brain stem: A phylogenetically older area of the brain consisting of the midbrain, metencephalon, and myelencephalon.

limbic system: A part of the brain most strikingly involved in emotion. Some major parts include the hippocampus, amygdala, hypothalamus, and septum.

Questions to Consider

1. What is the positive role of emotions in guiding action and decisions?

2. Compare the James-Lange theory of emotions with our expanded current understanding of how the brain and body influence emotional response.

Fear, Loathing, and Anger
Lecture 27

The hypothalamus is small; it's about the size of a large grape. It's less than 1% of the total volume of the human brain. Yet ... one can find all kinds of things packed within this very small structure.

Negative and very strong emotions are among those that regulate our behavior. Anger, fear, and anxiety originate in key brain structures that play a critical role in regulating strong emotions—the hypothalamus and the amygdala.

The hypothalamus, a central regulator of many of our most basic impulses, is less than 1% of the total volume of the human brain, yet it contains functions related to self-regulation and general emotional responses. It is a brain region, so its neurons send out axons, and it acts as a gland, so it secretes molecular signals in the form of hormones. These hormones coordinate the brain's and body's responses.

The amygdala can have a powerful suppressive effect on aggression, and it, too, seems to play a key role in driving strong emotional responses.

Let's just imagine for a moment that it's winter and that you're out hiking. You've been hiking a long way, and you're cold, dehydrated, low on energy. The hypothalamus takes signals from your viscera and your blood; processes them to make decisions about what to do; and starts sending signals about what should happen next. It will urge you to seek warmth, start moving around, drink water, and find some food.

The hypothalamus can also drive you powerfully to very intense responses. Experiments involving cutting into the brain and either leaving the hypothalamus attached to the brain stem or cutting it off from the brain stem have suggested that the hypothalamus plays a critical, necessary role for generating and controlling rage.

The amygdala can have a powerful suppressive effect on aggression, and it, too, seems to play a key role in driving strong emotional responses. It also organizes our responses to a possible danger stimulus, mediated by a rapid response from the visual system, and it can reduce physical signs of anxiety, such as sweating. This suggests that the amygdala is important in generating responses associated with fear.

The amygdala is also important in learning. A particular type of learning that involves fear conditioning has been studied in animals. It is possible to teach an animal, in a single trial, to be afraid of a neutral stimulus. But once learned, can fear memory be unlearned? It turns out that unlearning is much harder than learning in this case. Fear conditioning, evolutionarily, *must* be learned on a single trial because you might not get a second chance. Unlearning, however, requires many trials, and it seems to involve other structures, including the hippocampus and the neocortex.

Anxiety is closely related to fear. It is expressed in response to perceived danger as opposed to a specific event, such as whether we left the stove on when we left the house. The fear and anxiety system can malfunction to cause anxiety disorders, which can be debilitating. In anxiety disorders, the hypothalamic pituitary adrenal axis, the same axis involved in stress, shows a high level of activity. Anxiety disorders are marked by biochemical and neurological changes that are specific to the disorders, and one major hypothesis of anxiety disorder is that the axis malfunctions. It has been observed that maternal stress and the secretion of stress hormones are associated with later emotional problems, including anxiety disorders. This suggests that extreme stress in the mother can affect fetal brain development to influence the likelihood of an anxiety disorder. ∎

Questions to Consider

1. What is the difference between homeostasis and allostasis?

2. What are the allostatic roles of emotion and stress?

From Weather to Climate—Mood
Lecture 28

The weather can change from day to day, but climate takes much longer to change. Likewise, mood takes a longer time to change than emotion.

Moods are affected by environmental events: exposure to sunlight, the amount of sleep we get, our physical health. Examples of extreme moods can tell us something about the moods that we experience normally. Think of mood as a spectrum of possibilities, with mood disorders at the extreme of the spectrum. Mood, like emotion, depends on an interplay of signals between the body and the brain.

Symptoms of depression can be triggered by negative life events, such as bereavement, and by physical signals from the body, such as chronic pain. Depression as a mood disorder is recognizable by lowered mood and decreased interest or pleasure in all life activities. If these two symptoms are present every day for two weeks and no obvious life event, such as bereavement, has triggered the mood, the diagnosis is major depression.

Related to depression is bipolar syndrome, which includes depressive episodes interspersed with manic episodes that are characterized by inflated self-esteem or grandiosity, diminished need for sleep, talkativeness, racing thoughts, distractibility, and increased-goal directed activity. A milder form of mania is associated with increased efficiency, accomplishment, and creativity. Because people with bipolar syndrome often miss the manic episodes, getting them to stick with their medications can be difficult.

Several major theories and models attempt to explain what goes wrong in the brain that causes depression. One theory focuses on problems in monoamine neurotransmitters that are important in regulating mood, attention, sleep, and movement: dopamine, serotonin, adrenaline, and noradrenaline. The evidence that these molecules are involved in depression comes from drug treatments in which these neurotransmitters are manipulated pharmacologically. Blocking the breakdown of serotonin and noradrenaline with MAO inhibitors elevates mood, suggesting some role for monoamine transmitters in depression. Other pharmacological treatments include some antidepressant drugs that act directly on receptors in neurotransmitter pathways to manipulate neurotransmitter systems in the brain. One such drug influences GABA, an inhibitory neurotransmitter, by blocking GABA receptors.

Treatments that are effective for major depressive disorder include cognitive behavioral therapy, which applies specific techniques to dispel in patients negative evaluations of themselves, the world, and the future. Electroconvulsive therapy also has proven effective for major depression. It involves inducing seizures throughout the entire brain and can relieve symptoms for months. It is especially effective when paired with cognitive behavioral therapy.

Deep-brain stimulation can lead to nearly instantaneous changes in mood. The observation that depressive episodes are associated with activity in a thin strip of cortical tissue called the subgenual cingulate, or Area 25, led to a small study showing that stimulation of the **white matter** under Area 25 relieved symptoms in four out of six patients who were not helped by medication, electroconvulsive therapy, or psychotherapy.

Finally, a therapy that does not require brain surgery seems to be effective. It involves stimulation of the vagus nerve, part of the sympathetic nervous system, and helps about a third of patients who don't respond to antidepressants. The vagus nerve conveys information to the brain about body systems; thus, one hypothesis is that this treatment works because feelings of well-being may depend on the interplay between body and brain signals. This is reminiscent of the James-Lange theory that the brain sends signals to the body and the body sends physiological responses back to tell us what our mood is. ∎

Important Term

white matter: Axons; in the fresh brain, the myelin sheath surrounding axons gives it a "whitish" appearance.

1. Multiple treatment options are available for depression, including cognitive behavioral therapy and antidepressants. Discuss the pros and cons of these approaches. If it were you, which would you be inclined to try first?

2. What molecule does Prozac act upon in affecting mood? How does this work, and why does it take so long?

The Social Brain, Empathy, and Autism
Lecture 29

In our species, a major part of our identity depends on the fact that we're social animals, that we have this ability to imagine the thoughts of others. ... [This] ability to model other person's mental states and what other people might be thinking, this ability is necessary for us to navigate everyday life.

Theory of mind is observed in most children by age 3 or 4. It's possible to ask a 3-year-old, or even a younger child, why he or she was crying and receive a plausible answer. How does the theory of mind develop? A possible answer to this question lies in a developmental disorder in which the capacity for theory of mind seems to be absent: autism. Autism presents several classic signs: lack of social reciprocity, disrupted verbal and nonverbal communication, and inflexible and repetitive behaviors.

Autism is mostly a genetic disorder. The exact details of the genetic inheritance suggest that more than one gene is involved in autism, and many of these genes encode brain functions: perhaps proteins found in synapses or electrical signaling in neurons or in the development of the nervous system. One current area of challenge and research is to understand how these genetic variations combine to lead to autism.

Autistic people often show perceptual deficits, such as an inappropriate degree of sensitivity to routine sounds and even to the feel of their own clothing. The perceptual deficits by themselves are less germane than the possibility that they have a deeper meaning. Recent studies have shown that perceptual problems show up very early, even in 2-year-olds, and that these children show possible perceptual problems with biological motion. This is important because biological motion is a means by which we identify persons in our environment, as opposed to inanimate objects.

Perceptual problems in autistic children also appear in other aspects of life. For example, an autistic child listening to an adult tends to look at the adult's mouth rather than the eyes. This phenomenon suggests that perceptual problems may prevent autistic children from getting social cues in the first place. In fact, one possibility is that the perceptual problems might be a root cause of the difficulty babies and children have in forming social models. Other possibilities are that perceptual dysfunction and empathetic social deficits may share some common developmental issue important in generating both of these capacities.

One brain region where deficits are visible is the amygdala, which is important in processing emotional states of others and in generating emotional responses.

One brain region where deficits are visible is the amygdala, which is important in processing emotional states of others and in generating emotional responses. Another is the **cerebellum**, a brain structure that regulates movement and seems to be involved in detecting unexpected events. There has also been speculation about the insular cortex and mirror neurons, but evidence about the involvement of these brain regions is lacking.

One of the central challenges in neuroscience research in general is to understand different levels of function, understanding how molecules work together to generate functional synapses, how neurons talk with one another, how systems of circuits work together, and how the whole works together to make a working brain. Another area of current research is the study of how developmental processes coordinate these brain regions to work separately and together over development and throughout life to generate our many capacities and the ability to think about the motivations of other people. Autism is an active area of research both for its medical importance and at a fundamental level in understanding how these processes develop and how they can go wrong. ∎

Important Terms

cerebellum: Part of the metencephalon; involved in motor coordination and some cognitive functions.

theory of mind: The understanding that other individuals have different thoughts and knowledge than you; most frequently used as a term in child development.

Questions to Consider

1. What is theory of mind? Why would the amygdala be involved in this capacity?

2. What traits do autism and Asperger's syndrome share? What is known about the causes of these disorders?

Mars and Venus—Men's and Women's Brains
Lecture 30

The influence of the hypothalamus suggests a way for our brains to be connected to various phenomena that we think of as being separate from our mental processes.

B rain development is under the control of hormones; in the case of differences between the genders, these are sex hormones called **androgens** (male) and **estrogens** (female). Of course, as most of us know, men also make estrogens and women make androgens. These hormones are synthesized by cholesterol and converted by an enzymatic pathway to progesterone and then to testosterone. This chemical pathway shows that, in fact, these sex hormones are shared between men and women. Around the time of birth, sex hormones organize the brain by controlling the development of regions that will eventually become important for sexual behavior. During and after puberty, these behaviors are expressed by male and female hormones acting again.

In the brain, the hypothalamus activates the release of sex hormones in the pituitary. This is interesting because there is neocortical input to the hypothalamus, which means that psychological factors can influence fertility. In women, these hormones orchestrate the 28-day cycle, for example. The influence of the hypothalamus suggests that our brains are connected to various phenomena that we think of as being separate from our mental processes. There is some speculation that androgens and estrogens that increase in puberty might play a role in the mood and psychiatric disorders that appear at that time.

One area of gender differences that is perhaps the most politically fraught is cognitive abilities. Cognitive test performance measures, such as standardized examinations, demonstrate that math and verbal skills are, in fact, similar overall between men and women. This is true of a wide range of performance measures with a few exceptions. The only reliably measured difference between men and women is in manipulations having to do with space: spatial reasoning, memory, and navigation. When it comes to navigation, men tend to be oriented around the coordinates and women are oriented around landmarks.

Another area of contrast is that women tend to have significantly better spatial memory than men. Women are rather good at knowing where things are. The converse of that is in the mental rotation of objects, which is an area where men tend to do better than women. Some of this difference arises as a result of sex hormones acting throughout development, but some of it also happens in adulthood. For instance, amazingly, one shot of testosterone can improve female performance on an object rotation test.

One area of gender differences that is perhaps the most politically fraught is cognitive abilities.

The biggest cognitive difference between men and women is how they deal with spatial reasoning and spatial objects—how they deal with space. In addition, men and women differ in the frequency of neurological and psychiatric disorders. This phenomenon suggests that perhaps the normal ranges for men and women are somewhat different, and when we fall off the end of the range, we fall off in different ways. ■

Important Terms

androgens: A class of steroid hormones, including testosterone, with roles in aggression and sexual behavior in both sexes but most notably in males.

estrogen: A class of female reproductive hormones.

Questions to Consider

1. How do men and women differ in the way in which they deal with spatial relationships?

2. Are there any other significant gender differences in cognitive ability or mood?

Sex, Love, and Bonds for Life
Lecture 31

When we look at what happens during sexual behavior, it turns out ... the neural pathways that lead to sexual behavior ... involve quite similar neural circuits. ... In that respect, we're quite similar.

When we look at what happens during sexual behavior, the mechanics of sex—and by mechanics, we mean the neural pathways that lead to sexual behavior in men and women—involve quite similar neural circuits. Sexual performance requires the **sympathetic** and **parasympathetic nervous systems**, which push and pull our behavior in ways that are related to the stress system. What this means is that sexual performance is connected with the stress response. Stress has chronic effects on sexual behavior—for instance, in women, irregular menstrual cycles or even the cessation of menses and, in men, decreased sperm count and testosterone levels. For both men and women, interest in sexual behavior decreases with stress. Under conditions of stress, men often report problems with erections.

Orgasm itself has been imaged by Dutch scientists, who have found that the brain's reward system is activated during orgasm in both sexes, but there are differences between men and women. Women showed reduced activity in an area of the frontal cortex that might relate to a reduction of inhibition. Men showed reduced activity in the amygdala, where fear, anxiety, and vigilance arise. That suggests that during orgasm, men might experience a reduction in vigilance. Men and women shared increased activity in the cerebellum. The cerebellum has been implicated in emotional arousal and in sensory surprise, reflecting its role in reporting unexpected events.

One of the few reliable sex differences has been found in one particular area of the human hypothalamus, the third interstitial nucleus, which is twice as large in men as in women. A neuroscientist who has studied this nucleus in straight men and in gay men found that it was about half as large in gay men as in straight men. Although it's not at all known how this nucleus might be involved in generating sexual orientation, the fact that we can see these differences at all suggests the possibility of understanding preference as a biological mechanism.

Turning to the phenomenon of love, studies in voles have offered insight into how we form partnerships. In voles, the mechanism by which bonding occurs relies on vasopressin and **oxytocin**—major neuromodulator peptides made in the hypothalamus. They're also made in the ovaries or testes, and they play a critical role in pair bond formation. In the prairie vole, oxytocin released into the brain of a female during sexual activity is important for forming a monogamous pair bond with her sexual partner. Vasopressin appears to have a similar effect in males.

The cerebellum has been implicated in emotional arousal and in sensory surprise, reflecting its role in reporting unexpected events.

Returning to humans, during orgasm in women, oxytocin levels increase, and during sexual arousal in men, vasopressin concentrations increase. In addition, imaging experiments during romantic love show activation of reward areas, particularly regions that have receptors for oxytocin and vasopressin. These findings suggest that romantic love in humans and partnered pair bonding may involve oxytocin, vasopressin, and the brain's reward circuitry. The brain's reward areas, in the context of dopamine and addiction, are involved in the formation of addiction and in the signaling of reward. This suggests that release of dopamine may be critical for the response to such rewards as food, sex, and addictive drugs. One attractive possibility is that love, in some sense, may be the original addiction. ∎

Important Terms

oxytocin: The "love" molecule; a peptide hormone released by the hypothalamus; plays a role in a number of processes, including "bonding" in social animals.

parasympathetic nervous system: Part of the peripheral autonomic nervous system associated with "rest and digest" functions.

sympathetic nervous system: The part of the peripheral autonomic nervous system involved with the "fight or flight" response.

Questions to Consider

1. What biochemical signals are shared among sexual, familial, and trust-based bonding?

2. Is monogamy the norm or the exception among mammals? Birds?

Math and Other Evolutionary Curiosities
Lecture 32

> Why does humor exist and why [in] all these forms? ... It's not immediately clear how one could ever arrive at an adaptation-based explanation for these many forms of humor. After all, there's not really such a thing as a sarcastic rat or, for that matter, a sarcastic chimp.

A puzzle of human behavior is the existence of abilities in us with unknown survival value or with no clear antecedent among other animals—humor and math, for instance. Where did these capabilities come from, evolutionarily speaking? In general, the theory of natural selection posits that a selection advantage is necessary for a trait to become part of the heritage of a species.

Most behaviors have some antecedent in other animals: the fear response, the ability to detect and attract mates, the ability to pair bond, and the ability to avoid from danger. These behaviors have clear survival value and obviously measurable consequences. Two good examples of evolutionarily questionable capacities are humor and math. Why does humor exist, and why does it come in so many varieties? One can think of jokes, puns, slapstick, sarcasm, irony, and whimsy. Similarly, we have arithmetic, algebra, trigonometry, calculus, multivariate analysis, and the list goes on.

Humor may have its origins as a safety signal to others. Safety seems to be a feature of many forms of humor—slapstick, for example. It's a very primitive form of humor that is fundamentally based on the false appearance of injury. It's funny because there's a contradiction between the event and the actual hazard. Another possible explanation is that laughter is a signal to the social group that some event is of trivial consequence. This fits with the phenomenon that laughter is contagious in a group and with the idea of humor as a socially oriented safety signal.

More sophisticated humor involves cognition. A key component of a joke is a story that leads to a sudden flash of insight that happens in a moment when you have to reevaluate what was going on. Some patients with damage to the frontal lobes of the brain, in particular on the right side, don't get jokes at all, apparently because they have trouble with this reinterpretation stage of the process.

A harder question of evolutionary neuroscience is math. It appears that humans are unique in having the mental ability to do arithmetic. At its highest level, math is not seen in animals, but there are antecedents in other animals for certain rudimentary skills that go into math. The first is a sense of approximate number, or numerosity. If you look at a pile of objects, you can tell whether it has more or fewer than another pile. Another antecedent is an immediate sense of exact small numbers, or the ability to look at a number of objects and immediately know how many there are. This capability is called subitizing. These capacities have obvious selection advantages. It's easy to imagine that they are useful in the everyday life of any animal. They are thought to be the foundation of our sense of math.

Some traits, such as a bear's fur coat, have clear functional advantages.

What we share with animals is numerosity and subitizing. What is added that allows us to do arithmetic and, perhaps, higher math? The unique human contribution comes with symbolic representations of number, which is a component of language—a sense of exact number with associated symbols. Arithmetic and other forms of math seem to consist of linking this symbolic representation of number with the approximate number sense. ∎

Questions to Consider

1. What is the role of exaptation in accounting for the origins of a specific trait?

2. In this lecture, two specific advanced mental capacities were discussed: humor and mathematics. Are there mental functions that seem to you to be out of reach of an evolutionary explanation?

Consciousness and Free Will
Lecture 33

> What is it in the brain that produces the quality of "cold" or "blue"? ... What it is in the brain that produces this quality in the sense of what I feel, or perhaps what I imagine that you might feel? This seemingly simple question perplexes scientists partly because it defines the question in terms of unmeasurable aspects of experience.

The idea of **consciousness** contains two components: One is the state of being awake and able to respond to our environment, and the second is awareness of experience or thought. The fundamental concept for neuroscience in regard to consciousness is that a physical process of neural activity is responsible for the subjective phenomenon of awareness. This idea seems impossible; thus, there is some kind of fundamental gap to be bridged between the physical and the subjective. One approach is to seek a neural correlate of consciousness, a specific pattern of activity that correlates with a particular conscious experience.

Another way to think about consciousness is that it seems to have essential components. One is attention; another seems to be working memory, in the sense that when we are consciously aware, we can remember what happened before—a stream of consciousness. This combination seems to be a good provisional way to think about conscious awareness.

Conscious awareness may be overrated as a guide of behavior.

Conscious awareness may be overrated as a guide of behavior. For instance, our perception of the world is continuous, despite blinking or moving the eyes. We are able to discard that information because, if we perceived all that information, we would be distracted. The clear implication is that perception, while continuous, is in some sense a filtered version of what happens when we receive visual information from the world. The phenomenon of "blind sight," the ability of people with visual impairment to carry on activities of daily living, indicates that there are ways in which conscious awareness is unnecessary for navigating through the world.

The question of free will presents an apparent paradox to anyone interested in the philosophy of the brain. The physical model of how the brain works is that our experience, desires, thoughts, emotions, and reactions seem to be generated by the brain's physical activity. The implication is that physical and chemical laws govern all thoughts and actions: You are your brain. Yet every day, you make choices and act upon the world around you. How can these facts be reconciled?

The practical implications of what we know about brain function are perhaps less complicated than the philosophical contemplation of free will. A practical definition of free will is based on predictability. But even single synapses are unpredictable, so predicting the details of what a whole brain will do is impossible. From a practical standpoint, that's a definition of freedom and, perhaps, of free will.

In answer to the question of whether we should change the brain to influence behavior, the Dalai Lama said that such a treatment would have saved him time spent in meditation, freeing him up to do more good works. But he also said that such a treatment would be acceptable only if it left one's critical faculties intact.

This caveat raises the point of moral responsibility for our actions. For instance, is it possible to separate our actions from our capacity for moral reasoning? From the standpoint of everyday life, conceptual difficulties with the question of free will are resolved in a practical sense with the idea that you are responsible for all your actions. You are your brain and your brain is responsible for your actions. ∎

Important Term

consciousness: The awareness of oneself and the world in a subjective sense.

1. What does Benjamin Libet's experiment tell us about whether we have free will?

2. What is the role of punishment in our society for criminal actions? Do you think this role—or even punishment itself—may change in the future?

Near-Death and Other Extreme Experiences
Lecture 34

Out-of-body experiences happen in about 10% of the healthy population ... once or twice in a lifetime.

Mountaineers have long known to watch for the dangers of their sport, in particular when they're at high altitude, and they know to watch out for things that can happen in thin air. Many of the effects that they observe are attributable to the reduced supply of oxygen to the brain. At 2,500 meters or higher, some mountaineers report perceiving unseen companions, light emanating from themselves or from their body parts or the body parts of others, a second body like their own, or a figure where there is none. They suddenly feel such emotions as fear. The physical effects of mountain climbing, such as low oxygen, intense exertion, and stress, may account for these phenomena—they seem to increase, for instance, the likelihood of a seizure. Out-of-body experiences happen in about 10% of the healthy population, who have them once or twice in a lifetime. Evidence supports the idea that out-of-body experiences depend on the temporal parietal junction.

The temporal parietal junction of the brain seems to be involved in spatial self-perception and, thus, may be a candidate for understanding these phenomena. The parietal and temporal lobes sit on the brain surface close to the somata (body) sensory cortex, near where auditory and visual information comes in; thus, it seems well positioned to integrate

© iStockphoto/Thinkstock.

Mountain climbers can experience mental anomalies due to reduced supply of oxygen to the brain.

information from these sensory areas. There is also good evidence that this brain region is important for representations of the body.

Visions and visitations seem to be associated with the temporal lobe. The temporal and **parietal lobes** of the cortex are involved in visual and face processing, as well as emotional events. Oxygen deprivation is likely to interfere with activity in neural structures, and the temporal and parietal lobes seem particularly susceptible to oxygen deprivation. This association between oxygen deprivation and paranormal experiences may be associated with either temporal parietal seizures or temporal lobe seizures.

The phenomenon of haunted houses, common in the 19th and early 20th centuries, is associated with using gas for house lighting: a source of carbon monoxide emission. Carbon monoxide binds to hemoglobin, the molecule that carries oxygen in the blood and leads to oxygen deprivation to the brain. Reports of haunted houses have diminished considerably now that gas is no longer used to light houses.

Near-death experiences are characterized by the feeling of leaving your physical body and seeing your life flashing before you. They have been estimated to happen in 9–18% of persons near the point of death. One possible explanation is that general oxygen deprivation can lead to widespread activity throughout the brain, and it's easy to imagine that this kind of activity could account for accelerated thought processes.

All the different kinds of brain activity triggered by various events, from seizures to dreams, require the brain to convert them into a storyline. One unifying explanation is that the brain is engaging in some kind of confabulation to piece together a story from incomplete or highly unusual data. ∎

Important Term

parietal lobe: A cortical lobe bordered by the central sulcus of Rolando anteriorly, the parieto-occipital sulcus posteriorly, and the Sylvian (lateral) fissure inferiorly.

1. What common factor(s) may underlie visions at altitude and haunted-house visitations?

2. How might low blood oxygen during a near-death experience lead to the feeling of "life review"?

Spirituality and Religion
Lecture 35

The ability to cooperate and to compete with our fellow beings may have set the stage for forming religious mental constructs.

W hen Buddhists talk about meditation, they divide it into two major categories: stilling the mind, or stabilizing meditation, and a process of understanding, meditating on an object or meditating on an idea—discursive meditation. Investigators have studied the first category in Buddhist monks who are well practiced in the process of objectless meditation by measuring patterns of electrode activity. At first, those patterns were no different from those of volunteers who were meditating for the first time. But when asked to generate a feeling of compassion, the brains of experienced practitioners began varying in a coherent rhythmic oscillation, suggesting that many neural structures were firing in synchrony with one another, a phenomenon called gamma rhythm. Several types of rhythm seem to get stronger with experience in novices who learn meditation, which suggests that the capacity is at least partly trainable. Similarly, prayer might benefit the person doing the praying just as meditation benefits or changes the brain patterns of these Buddhist monks. That is to say, prayer might benefit us in a process that transforms our mental state.

Anthropologists have studied religion around the world

© iStockphoto/Thinkstock.

Prayer, like meditation, can change the practitioner's brain state.

and found that having religion offers advantages—in particular, religion is a powerful early instrument of group social bonding, and it has been suggested that this social bonding presents some kind of competitive advantage to help the group survive. Religion is a highly sophisticated cultural phenomenon involving many components. Brain capabilities important for forming and transmitting religious beliefs include the search for causes and effects, social reasoning, and language and the cultural transmission of information.

Social communication requires such structures as the amygdala, which is intimately involved in deriving the emotional significance of objects and faces and, thus, is critical in giving the brain access to the mental states of others. These forms of social complexity seem to be related to the size of the **cerebral cortex**. The ability to cooperate and to compete with our fellow beings may have set the stage for forming religious mental constructs.

The notion that accumulated ideas could be modified, allowing a doctrine and a dogma to be communicated and preserved from generation to generation, requires language, an aspect that is less well understood from a neuroscientific standpoint but important in terms of what makes religious belief possible. Our capacity for language allows our search for causes and effects to take on a new dimension in the form of narrative.

Any eventual neuroscientific explanation of how we form narratives is likely to address how narratives lead us to believe a story. For example, how exactly would an omniscient omnipotent being run the world? One point of view is that God would put every detail in place. But another point of view might be that God works through amazing processes, such as natural selection and brains. Rather than having to supervise everything from moment to moment, perhaps God launched natural processes to ensure the functioning of creation. In this respect, neuroscience is a way of understanding more deeply the world around us. ■

Important Term

cerebral cortex: The outer sheet or mantle of cells covering the hemispheres.

1. What brain capacities are necessary in order to be able to form a belief in God?

2. In light of known brain mechanisms, how might prayer have an effect, and in whose brain?

Happiness and Other Research Opportunities
Lecture 36

It turns out that you never adapt to commuting to work. ... It's always going to make you, on average, a little bit less happy.

Surveys on happiness tell us some interesting things—for example, that happiness is strongly dependent, not on income, but on *relative* wealth. Happiness also is stable over time, despite the fact that our life circumstances obviously change. On whether major life events make us happy or unhappy in the long term, findings are somewhat surprising. Being married is correlated with happiness, but having children, according to these surveys, doesn't make us any happier.

Many results seem to be consistent with the concept of the hedonic treadmill: the idea that happiness seems to adapt and to have a set point. The general concept is that events that affect happiness are mostly temporary, so people quickly adapt back to hedonic neutrality. But some circumstances are reliably associated with unhappiness or with happiness. Affiliation with a religious or political group increases happiness, for example. But it turns out that you never adapt to commuting to work. It's always going to make you a little cranky.

Another principle is that one person may have many set points. At one stage of your emotional awareness, you might have different components of well-being, and these can move in different directions over life. These components not only vary over time but also in response to persistent positive or negative events and factors. Finally, our ability to adapt to events seems to vary by individuals. Strategies for increasing happiness in the face of this hedonic treadmill include the following:

- Finding ways to beat adaptation by experiencing frequent small events that are less likely to "adapt out" than one large event that then leads to a return to the set point.

- Focusing on positive events.

- Identifying character strengths and using them.

- Remembering to be grateful.

What's missing in this discussion is a good explanation of neuroscientific mechanisms, biological mechanisms, of what determines happiness. Accidental discoveries from neuroscience are relevant to this discussion of happiness. There are some surprising ways in which neuroscience could be useful. Current research is altering technologies that allow us to probe and study the brain in ways that we previously could not. Modern molecular biology methods allow us to alter the functions of neurons, build viruses that drive the expression of some proteins in neurons, and even cross synapses.

Technology similar to that used to locate seizure areas can be applied to develop brain-machine interfaces, like neural prosthetics. It's possible to achieve some crude degree of control over an artificial limb by decoding a person's motor commands. What that suggests is that technologically, it may become possible someday to restore some degree of function using brain-machine interfaces.

Other new fields are optogenetics, a means of manipulating a neuron by having it express its protein genetically and then applying light, and connectomics, the idea of deciphering and reconstructing an entire circuit: the connections, their physical arrangement, and the biochemical details.

All these technologies are at the cutting edge. It's reasonable to say that it's within reach for us to start understanding, at all levels, ranging from cognition and behavior to cells and circuits, what our brains are doing when we learn, when we love, and when we experience everyday life. ∎

Questions to Consider

1. What factors influence the hedonic treadmill? What major factors in your life seem likely to affect your happiness in the long run?

2. How do you imagine the new technologies described in this lecture (and yet undiscovered technologies) will affect the study of the brain?

Glossary

acetylcholine: A neurotransmitter whose functions include release from the ends of the final neurons in the parasympathetic nervous system.

action potential: A change in membrane potential arising at the axon hillock; it travels down the axon in an all-or-none fashion.

adrenal glands: Glands located above the kidneys; under stress, they release catecholamines and cortisol.

Alzheimer's disease: A degenerative neurological disorder characterized primarily by the loss of neurons in higher-order regions of the neocortex, limbic system structures, and specific reticular formation nuclei with widespread projections to the cortex.

amino acids: The building blocks of proteins; about 20 different kinds, akin to letters, exist. Unique sequences of amino acids are strung together to form a particular protein. That sequence determines the folded shape of that protein and, thus, its function.

amygdala: An almond-shaped nucleus beneath the rostral pole of the temporal lobe; involved in the processing of emotions, particularly fear.

androgens: A class of steroid hormones, including testosterone, with roles in aggression and sexual behavior in both sexes but most notably in males. (See also **anabolic hormones**.)

autonomic nervous system (ANS): A series of neural pathways originating in the hypothalamus, hindbrain, and brainstem and projecting throughout the body; it regulates all sorts of nonconscious, automatic physiological changes throughout the body. The ANS consists of the sympathetic and parasympathetic nervous systems.

axon: The process of a neuron specialized for the transmission of information; axons are the physical structures that connect different areas of the brain.

basal ganglia: A number of nuclei located subcortically in the forebrain. Many of the basal ganglia nuclei are involved in the extrapyramidal motor system.

biogenic amines: In the context of how the term is used in this course, it refers to the monoamine neurotransmitters dopamine, norepinephrine, and serotonin.

bipolar disorder (manic depression): An illness characterized by wide mood swings ranging from severe depression to expansive mania.

brain stem: A phylogenetically older area of the brain consisting of the midbrain, metencephalon, and myelencephalon.

central nervous system (CNS): The part of the nervous system comprising the brain and spinal cord.

cerebellum: Part of the metencephalon; involved in motor coordination and some cognitive functions.

cerebral cortex: The outer sheet or mantle of cells covering the hemispheres.

cochlea: Fluid-filled structure of the inner ear.

cognitive/cognition: Related to mental activities such as thinking, learning, and memory.

consciousness: The awareness of oneself and the world in a subjective sense.

dementia: A progressive mental deterioration.

dendrite: The part of the neuron that receives signals from other neurons. Dendrites tend to come in the form of highly branched cables coming from the cell body of a neuron.

depression: A disorder of "mood" characterized by an internal subjective state of hopelessness and despair.

dopamine: A neurotransmitter whose functions include a role in sequential thought (such that abnormal dopamine levels are associated with the disordered thought of schizophrenia), the anticipation of pleasure, and aspects of fine motor control.

emotion: A basic, physiological state characterized by identifiable autonomic or bodily changes.

epinephrine (a.k.a. adrenaline): Both a neurotransmitter throughout the brain and a hormone released in the adrenal gland during stress as a result of activation of the sympathetic nervous system.

estrogen: A class of female reproductive hormones.

evolution: When referring to biological systems specifically, a change in allele frequencies over time in a genetically continuous population of organisms.

frontal cortex: A recently evolved region of the brain that plays a central role in executive cognitive function, decision making, gratification postponement, and regulation of the limbic system.

gamma-aminobutyric acid (GABA): A major inhibitory neurotransmitter of the CNS, particularly of interneurons.

ganglion (pl. ganglia): A group of cell bodies in the peripheral nervous system; comparable to a nucleus in the central nervous system. Some structures in the central nervous system (e.g., basal ganglia) are also referred to as ganglia.

gene: A stretch of DNA that designates the construction of one protein.

glial cells: An accessory type of cell found in the nervous system. Glial cells support neuronal function by insulating the axons of neurons, indirectly supplying neurons with energy, scavenging dead neurons, and removing toxins from the extracellular space around neurons. (Contrast with **neurons**.)

glucocorticoids: A class of steroid hormones secreted during stress. They include cortisol (a.k.a. hydrocortisone) and synthetic versions, such as prednisone and dexamethasone.

glutamate: An excitatory neurotransmitter with critical roles in learning and memory. An excess of glutamate induces *excitotoxicity*, a route by which neurons are killed during various neurological insults.

gray matter: Areas where there are collections of neuronal cell bodies.

hippocampus: A brain region within the limbic system that plays a central role in learning and memory.

homeostasis: "Balance"; as used here, for example, balance between sympathetic and parasympathetic portions of the autonomic nervous system.

homunculus: Distorted figure of a "man" mapped onto brain regions in motor and somatosensory areas.

hormones: Blood-borne chemical messengers between cells.

hypothalamus: A limbic structure that receives heavy inputs from other parts of the limbic system; plays a central role in regulating both the autonomic nervous system and hormone release.

ion channel: Generally a protein that regulates the flow of ions, for example, across a membrane.

limbic system: A part of the brain most strikingly involved in emotion. Some major parts include the hippocampus, amygdala, hypothalamus, and septum.

magnetic resonance imaging (MRI)/functional magnetic resonance imaging (fMRI): A computer-assisted imaging that uses powerful magnets to create detailed images of soft tissue; functional MRI refers to the additional method of visualizing what areas of the brain are active or functional by their utilization of oxygen.

mutation: An error in the copying of a gene. Classically, mutations can take three forms: In *point mutations*, a letter in the DNA code is misread as a different letter. In *deletion mutations*, a letter is entirely lost. In *insertion mutations*, an extra letter is inserted.

natural selection: The process by which competition for limited resources causes the preservation or elimination of particular alleles.

neuron: Specialized cells of the nervous system.

neurotransmitter: Small molecules used by the brain to transmit signals across synapses from one neuron to another.

norepinephrine (a.k.a. noradrenaline): A neurotransmitter whose functions include release from the ends of the final neurons in the sympathetic nervous system, as well as a role in depression (with, most likely, a depletion occurring).

opioids: Naturally occurring "morphine-like" peptides in the brain.

orbitofrontal cortex: A part of the frontal lobe involved in impulse control, inculcation of cultural mores, and ability to appreciate the consequences of one's behavior.

oxytocin: The "love" molecule; a peptide hormone released by the hypothalamus; plays a role in a number of processes, including "bonding" in social animals.

parasympathetic nervous system: Part of the peripheral autonomic nervous system associated with "rest and digest" functions.

parietal lobe: A cortical lobe bordered by the central sulcus of Rolando anteriorly, the parieto-occipital sulcus posteriorly, and the Sylvian (lateral) fissure inferiorly.

Parkinson's disease: A neurodegenerative disease resulting from the loss of neurons in the substantia nigra of the midbrain; characterized by a resting tremor, abnormal posture, and paucity of normal movement.

perception: The mental process or act of awareness of an object or idea.

positron emission tomography (PET): An imaging method utilizing radioactive tagged glucose or oxygen to examine the metabolism and activity of neurons.

post-traumatic stress disorder (PTSD): A disorder characterized by anxiety and fear acquired because of a traumatic event.

prefrontal cortex: Part of the frontal lobe implicated in working memory.

protein: One of 5 categories of organic molecules present in all organisms. A protein consists of a chain of amino acids, the sequence of which is determined by information encoded in the genome. Proteins can act as enzymes and/or as structural components of organisms.

receptor: A protein that binds to other molecules, for example, a neurotransmitter; also the name given to various types of sensory neurons that respond to particular modalities, for example, rods and cones are visual sensory receptor neurons.

retina (neural retina): Multilayered sheet of neurons located at the back of the eyeball, and derived from the diencephalon in development.

retinal ganglion cells (RGCs): The neurons whose axons leave the eye to project to a variety of structures in the brain, including the lateral geniculate nucleus of the thalamus.

scientific method: The use of data collection, measurement, or other forms of experimentation followed by statistical analysis to determine objectively whether evidence exists to support or reject a scientific hypothesis.

sensation: The result of stimulation of sense organs; can also be a "feeling" in the somatosensory system.

serotonin: A neurotransmitter whose functions include a role in aggression, sleep onset, depression, and impulsivity.

stroke: Any acute neurological event related to impairment in blood flow or circulation in the central nervous system; can be hemorrhagic or ischemic.

sympathetic nervous system: The part of the peripheral autonomic nervous system involved with the "fight or flight" response.

synapse: Specialized contact between 2 neurons that allows one to send signals to the other.

synaptic plasticity: The dynamic property of synapses; believed to underlie learning and memory.

thalamus: A major structure of the diencephalon; composed of a number of individual nuclei, many of which project to the cortex, giving it the name "anteroom."

theory of mind: The understanding that other individuals have different thoughts and knowledge than you; most frequently used as a term in child development.

white matter: Axons; in the fresh brain, the myelin sheath surrounding axons gives it a "whitish" appearance.

Bibliography

The following two books provide a good introduction to neuroscience:

Aamodt, Sandra, and Sam Wang. *Welcome to Your Brain: Why You Lose Your Car Keys but Never Forget How to Drive and Other Puzzles of Everyday Life.* New York: Bloomsbury USA, 2009.

Bear, Mark F., Barry W. Connors, and Michael A. Paradiso. *Neuroscience: Exploring the Brain.* Baltimore: Lippincott Williams & Wilkins, 2006.

In addition, good resources exist for following current neuroscience news, including the magazine *Scientific American Mind* and several Web blogs:

Mind Hacks. http://www.mindhacks.com/.

Neurophilosophy. http://scienceblogs.com/neurophilosophy/.

The Neurocritic. http://neurocritic.blogspot.com/.

General Interest

Breedlove, S. M., Mark R. Rosenzweig, and Neil V. Watson. *Biological Psychology: An Introduction to Behavioral, Cognitive, and Clinical Neuroscience.* Ann Arbor, MI: Sinauer Associates, 2007. A college-level textbook on psychological phenomena treated from a neuroscientific point of view.

Gross, Charles G. *A Hole in the Head: More Tales in the History of Neuroscience.* Cambridge, MA: MIT Press, 2009. General essays on topics in the history of neuroscience, including trepanation, left-right asymmetry, and adult neurogenesis.

Linden, David J. *The Accidental Mind: How Brain Evolution Has Given Us Love, Memory, Dreams, and God.* Cambridge, MA: Belknap Press of Harvard University Press, 2008. A neuroscientist considers the brain not as a carefully engineered machine but, with all its imperfections and foibles, as the complex outcome of contingent events over the course of evolution.

Ramachandran, V. S., and Sandra Blakeslee. *Phantoms in the Brain: Probing the Mysteries of the Human Mind.* New York: Harper Perennial, 1999. A neurologist and a neuroscience writer together consider the strange quirks that emerge when the pain of a missing limb is caused by the lingering presence of its representation in the brain. [Suggested reading for Lectures 7, 8, and 9.]

Specific Topics

Aamodt, Sandra, and Sam Wang. "Tighten Your Belt, Strengthen Your Mind." *New York Times*, April 2, 2008, p. A27 (op-ed). [Suggested reading for Lecture 15.]

Basso, Olga. "Right or Wrong? On the Difficult Relationship between Epidemiologists and Handedness." *Epidemiology* 18 (March 2007):191–193. [Suggested reading for Lecture 21.]

Bauby, Jean-Dominique. *The Diving Bell and the Butterfly: A Memoir of Life in Death.* New York: Vintage, 1998. A memoir of locked-in syndrome; the basis for the film of the same title.

Blanke, Olaf, Christine Mohr, Christoph M. Michel, Alvaro Pascual-Leone, Peter Brugger, Margitta Seeck, Theodor Landis, and Gregor Thut. "Linking Out-of-Body Experience and Self Processing to Mental Own-Body Imagery at the Temporoparietal Junction." *Journal of Neuroscience* 25 (2005):550–557. [Suggested reading for Lecture 34.]

Buckner, Randy L. "Memory and Executive Function in Aging and AD: Multiple Factors That Cause Decline and Reserve Factors That Compensate." *Neuron* 44 (2004):195–208. [Suggested reading for Lectures 22 and 23.]

Chawla, Lakhmir S., Seth Akst, Christopher Junker, Barbara Jacobs, and Michael G. Seneff. "Surges of Electroencephalogram Activity at the Time of Death: A Case Series." *Journal of Palliative Medicine* 12 (2009): 1095–1100. [Suggested reading for Lecture 34.]

Colcombe, Stanley and Arthur F. Kramer. "Fitness Effects on the Cognitive Function of Older Adults: A Meta-Analytic Study." *Psychological Science* 14 (2003):125–130. [Suggested reading for Lecture 23.]

Damasio, Antonio. *Descartes' Error: Emotion, Reason, and the Human Brain*. New York: Penguin, 2005. [Suggested reading for Lectures 26, 27, and 28.]

Dehaene, Stanislas. *The Number Sense: How the Mind Creates Mathematics*. New York: Oxford University Press, USA, 1999. [Suggested reading for Lecture 32.]

Diamond, Adele, W. Steven Barnett, Jessica Thomas, and Sarah Munro. "Preschool Program Improves Cognitive Control." *Science* 318 (2007):1387–1388. [Suggested reading for Lecture 18.]

Doidge, Norman. *The Brain That Changes Itself: Stories of Personal Triumph from the Frontiers of Brain Science*. New York: Penguin, 2007. [Suggested reading for Lectures 7, 8, 12, and 13.]

Flynn, James R. *What Is Intelligence? Beyond the Flynn Effect*. New York: Cambridge University Press, 2009. [Suggested reading for Lecture 25.]

Gilbert, Daniel. *Stumbling on Happiness*. New York: Vintage, 2007. [Suggested reading for Lectures 10 and 36.]

Gopnik, Alison. *The Philosophical Baby: What Children's Minds Tell Us about Truth, Love, and the Meaning of Life*. New York: Farrar, Straus and Giroux, 2009. [Suggested reading for Lectures 18 and 19.]

Gradinaru, Viviana, Murtaza Mogri, Kimberly R. Thompson, Jaimie M. Henderson, and Karl Deisseroth. "Optical Deconstruction of Parkinsonian

Neural Circuitry." *Science* 324 (2009): 354–359. [Suggested reading for Lecture 36.]

Harris, Judith Rich. *The Nurture Assumption: Why Children Turn Out the Way They Do*. New York: Free Press, 2009. [Suggested reading for Lectures 18, 19, 20, 24, and 25.]

Kandel, Eric R. *In Search of Memory: The Emergence of a New Science of Mind*. New York: W.W. Norton & Co., 2007.

Katz, Bernard. *Nerve, Muscle and Synapse*. New York: McGraw-Hill, 1966. [Suggested reading for Lecture 4.]

LeDoux, Joseph. *The Emotional Brain: The Mysterious Underpinnings of Emotional Life*. New York: Simon & Schuster, 1998. [Suggested reading for Lectures 26, 27, and 28.]

Levitin, Daniel J. *This Is Your Brain on Music: The Science of a Human Obsession*. New York: Plume/Penguin, 2007. [Suggested reading for Lecture 32.]

Marcus, Gary. *Kluge: The Haphazard Evolution of the Human Mind*. New York: Mariner Books, 2009. [Suggested reading for Lectures 3 and 10.]

Panda, Satchidananda, John B. Hogenesch, and Steve A. Kay. "Circadian Rhythms from Flies to Human." *Nature* 417 (2002):329–335.

Risley, Todd R., and Betty Hart. *Meaningful Differences in the Everyday Experience of Young American Children*. Baltimore, MD: Paul H. Brookes Publishing Co., 1995. [Suggested reading for Lectures 18 and 19.]

Sacks, Oliver. *Awakenings*. New York: Vintage, 1999. [Suggested reading for Lectures 5 and 6.]

Sapolsky, Robert M. *Why Zebras Don't Get Ulcers*. New York: Holt Paperbacks, 2004. [Suggested reading for Lecture 16.]

Bibliography

Schacter, Daniel L. *Searching for Memory: The Brain, the Mind, and the Past*. New York: Basic Books, 1997. [Suggested reading for Lectures 12, 13, and 14.]

Schwartz, Barry. *The Paradox of Choice: Why More Is Less*. New York: Harper Perennial, 2005. [Suggested reading for Lectures 10 and 36.]

Smith, Christian. *Moral, Believing Animals: Human Personhood and Culture*. New York: Oxford University Press USA, 2009. [Suggested reading for Lecture 35.]

Snyder, Solomon H. *Drugs and the Brain*. Scientific American Library Series, vol. 18. New York: W.H. Freeman & Company, 1996. [Suggested reading for Lectures 5 and 6.]

Thagard, Paul. *The Brain and the Meaning of Life*. Princeton: Princeton University Press, 2010. [Suggested reading for Lectures 33 and 35.]

Notes

Notes

Notes

Notes

Notes

Notes

Notes